# North American
# BIRDS OF PREY

# North American
# BIRDS OF PREY

## ALEXANDER SPRUNT, Jr. D.Sc.

of the National Audubon Society Staff, Fellow of the
American Ornithologists' Union

Based upon and Supplementary to *The Hawks of North America,*
by John Bichard May. Color plates from original paintings by Allan
Brooks and others, black and white illustrations by Roger Tory
Peterson

*With a Foreword by*
### ROGER TORY PETERSON

*Published under the sponsorship of*
### THE NATIONAL AUDUBON SOCIETY

## BONANZA BOOKS • NEW YORK

NORTH AMERICAN BIRDS OF PREY

*Copyright © MCMLV by The National Audubon Society*
*Printed in the United States of America*

All rights in this book are reserved.
No part of the book may be used or reproduced
in any manner whatsoever without written permission except in the case of brief quotations
embodied in critical articles and reviews.

*This edition published by Bonanza Books,*
*a division of Crown Publishers, Inc., by*
*arrangement with Harper & Row, Publish-*
*ers, Incorporated.*
A B C D E F G

*Library of Congress catalog card number: 55-8557*

# Contents

# Foreword

## by ROGER TORY PETERSON

King Solomon, wisest of men, concluded that among the many things too wonderful to understand was "the way of an eagle in the air."

There were far more eagles in Biblical days. The ancients must have been familiar with these masters of the sky, soaring high on the thermals. In pre-Columbian times there were more eagles in North America, that is certain, and also many more of the lesser hawks; the number of raptores has gone into a steep decline—inversely to the rise in human population.

Most Americans have never seen a wild Bald Eagle, the national emblem of the United States, and it is likely that as time goes on the percentage of those who have seen one will be even smaller. The National Audubon Society recently reported with alarm that there may now be fewer than 1,000 pairs of Bald Eagles remaining within the borders of the United States. (West Florida's eagles have suffered an 80 per cent decline in a decade, mostly from real estate development, the disappearance of big nest trees, and illegal shooting.) Golden Eagles, shot from small planes in Texas and in other western states, are disappearing from the skies at an even faster rate.

The raptores, of all birds the finest, are like masterworks of art —yet they are subjected during their fall migration, and at other seasons too, to a barrage comparable to that directed at the clay pigeons in a shooting gallery. How long would the treasures of the Metropolitan Museum or the National Gallery last if they were treated in such a manner? It is a miracle that our hawks, owls, and eagles have hung on as well as they have, but how long can they continue to do so? I no longer see anywhere near the number of hawks that gave lift to my spirit when I was a boy, thirty years ago, and it is not because my eyes are no longer as efficient.

All through the ages, until recent times, these virile birds were regarded as something very special. In falconry, the possession of Peregrines, Goshawks, and Gyrfalcons was reserved for the nobility. Each species had its rank. In fact the name hawk was used only for the accipitrine birds of prey—those with short rounded wings and longish tails—the bird eaters such as the Cooper's hawk, Sharp-shin, and Goshawk. The first settlers in the New World were not naturalists; poorly informed, they ignored or did not know most of the colorful old English names such as Peregrine, Kestrel, Merlin, and Harrier, and they applied the term hawk to nearly all the day-flying raptores except the eagles. The term buzzard (which should have been applied to our wide-winged Buteos, such as the Red-shouldered and Red-tailed Hawks) they gave to the new-world vultures.

Because the name hawk originally belonged to the bird-eating Accipiters, all birds of prey, even the mouse-eating sorts, were branded with the stigma attached to that name. Men with guns soon began to regard any birds with hooked beaks and hooked claws not as fellow hunters to be admired for their native abilities, but as competitors, ever on the lookout for game to poach. Contemptuously they were branded "vermin," to be shot at every opportunity, even though most of them seldom winked a predatory eye at a quail or a pheasant.

In 1893 a book published by the United States Department of Agriculture changed the point of view of many conservationists and was to influence their thinking for the next half century. *The Hawks and Owls of the United States in Their Relation to Agriculture* by Dr. A. K. Fisher urged farmers to protect the majority of the birds of prey and gave, as evidence in their behalf, the results of an exhaustive study of the feeding habits of 32 species of hawks and 17 species of owls, based on the stomach contents of 2,690 birds. Measured by this yardstick, most species were rated as "beneficial" and only a few were regarded as definitely "harmful."

That these stomach-content evaluations were useful for a time cannot be denied. The word "ecology" was unknown until relatively recently and the phrase "balance of nature" was only a vague concept. But in the long run it has become evident that the food-chart idea has perhaps outlived its usefulness and might indeed be a retarding device in explaining the true role of the predator. By separating the sheep from the goats, it becomes inevitable that certain birds are labeled "good" and others "bad," whereas every informed field biologist now knows that such classification is too simple, indeed false. No bird or other wild creature is either "good" or "bad," but simply lives its life according to its attributes and the rules laid down for its kind by its Creator. Biologists, slowly digging out the facts, are discovering more and more about the balance between the animal and its environment—the balance of nature that we hear so much about (a swinging balance, it is true). If one kind of prey becomes hard to get, the animal turns to something else; availability determines much of its diet. In short, natural predators have no basic effect upon the population level of the species on which they prey but merely crop the surpluses which would be trimmed off anyway by other natural agents— disease, hunger, and interspecific competition. Predators (even a robin is a predator—on worms) live on the interest and do not eat deep into capital. In fact, the higher predators are believed to tone up the vitality of the stock by weeding out the weaker or less capable individuals. Man, in fact, is one of the few predators in the world so efficient that he sometimes completely eliminates the species on which he preys.

Hawk Mountain in Pennsylvania and Cape May in New Jersey have, during the last twenty years, done much to publicize the desirability of preserving our hawks. This book's predecessor, *The Hawks of North America,* published in 1935, has also had a twenty-year history and did a very fine job of presenting the birds of prey on the basis of examinations of stomachs and crops. This new volume meets the times by presenting the magnificent but maligned birds of prey in the new light shed by recent ecological research.

Keep the hawks and owls flying!

# Introduction*

Probably there is no avian family which through the ages has been subjected to such extremes of admiration and condemnation as the birds of prey. Revered and respected on the one hand, they have been elevated to representing empires, kingdoms, and republics; on the other hand they have been vilified, persecuted, and slaughtered. Although they embody such appealing qualities as fearlessness, audacity, speed, and beauty, these birds have been considered by many people to be hostile to human interests and consequently have been decimated in a senseless and ruthless manner.

Throughout history man has been keenly aware of the admirable qualities of the birds of prey. Imperial Rome set the eagle upon the standards of its legions; the Vikings adorned their helmets with the wings of hawks, while from eastern mountains to western plains and canyons, Cherokee, Sioux and Apache selected flawless plumage of eagle and hawk for headdress. In our day, the Caracara dominates the State Seal of Mexico while the Bald Eagle is the emblem of the United States.

Despite the official honors that have been heaped upon them, the birds of prey have not fared so well at the hands of the average man. A hawk soars over his farmyard and the man with the hoe rushes for his trusty shooting iron. A hunter roaming the October woods flushes a Horned Owl that has been dozing in a tree; he shoots it and congratulates himself upon having dispatched a "fierce and vicious" killer that he fancies is directly competing

---

* Portions of this introduction are derived from the booklet, "Birds of Prey," by Kenneth D. Morrison, published in 1954 by Nelson Doubleday, Inc. I am grateful to the author and publisher for permission to use this material.—A. S., Jr.

with him for grouse and other game. By what logic it is "vicious" for a Horned Owl to kill a rabbit, but an act of rugged sportsmanship when the deed is done by a man, has never been very satisfactorily explained. A rancher surveying his grazing lands from a plane spots a floating speck in the sky that turns out to be a Golden Eagle wheeling gracefully, its gaze intent upon a ground squirrel that would make a succulent meal. The rancher recalls lurid tales of eagle depredations upon livestock, so he shoulders his gun and draws a bead; the great golden bird plummets earthward. The man in the plane did not thrill to the magnificent powers of flight of the eagle, far more wondrous than those of his mechanical bird. Obviously he would not agree with naturalist Olaus Murie that a dead eagle is both an economic and a spiritual loss.

Another well-known naturalist, Aldo Leopold, expressed it this way: "The swoop of a hawk . . . is perceived by one as the drama of evolution. To another it is only a threat to the full frying pan. The drama may thrill a hundred successive witnesses; the threat only one—for he responds with a shotgun."

Hawks and owls have never had an easy life. Both groups have been persecuted widely, hawks more so than owls. Hawks are day-flying birds, and most of the owls are nocturnal, so man is less aware of the activities of the latter.

Many of the birds of prey have been seriously reduced in numbers—the most conspicuous and least adaptable ones having suffered the most. One of these, the California Condor, is now the third rarest species on this continent. Another, the Everglade Kite, is close behind the Condor in fourth place. Even our national emblem, the Bald Eagle, has disappeared from much of its former range and, despite federal protection, is still thoughtlessly destroyed. It seems reasonable to assume that if the present trend continues, the United States may before long face the prospect of being represented by an extinct emblem. It is ironic indeed to deny freedom to the symbol of freedom.

How did prejudice against the predatory birds develop? Game farms had a lot to do with it. English gamekeepers early developed the concept that anything which "competed" with game should be regarded as "vermin" and liquidated. This idea was imported into the United States and Canada and prevailed up until fairly recent years.

It should be remembered that game farms produce abnormal concentrations of birds in open pens completely lacking in escape cover such as briar patches and shrubbery. This situation allows even the slowest of hawks to dine on birds that are usually too swift for the raptores to capture in a natural environment. Many a gamekeeper makes his generalizations about predation from the highly artificial situation he creates on his game farm.

The development of wildlife research as a profession probably did more than anything else to quash the gamekeepers' ideas about the birds of prey. Professional game managers discovered that the key to wildlife abundance is food and cover. They found that under normal conditions predators exert a negligible influence in determining the abundance of game. They pointed out that in some instances predators actually aid the game by helping to control the populations of rodents which sometimes prey upon the eggs and young of game birds. They stated, too, that predators are responsible for developing alertness and speed in game species—characteristics that most certainly make them of interest to sportsmen.

Hunters have been slow to accept what some regard as impractical theories, but actual experimentation by state and federal conservation agencies has proved that the theories are based on fact. There are few game managers today who will deny that, if the environmental conditions are right, game will thrive, and if conditions are inadequate, game will be scarce regardless of how intensely the predatory birds and mammals are destroyed.

Richard H. Pough, president of the Nature Conservancy and author of the *Audubon Bird Guides,* in his travels as a biologist and ecologist has noted that in relatively primitive, undisturbed wild areas, both game birds and hawks have seemed unusually abundant. He adds that a careful analysis of the interplay of one species on another within the wildlife community reveals a number of reasons for believing that game and hawk abundance may be linked far more closely than has ever been realized.

Sportsmen's organizations which not long ago found it impossible to say anything good about the birds of prey are now speaking up in defense of the predators and urging their members not to kill these birds indiscriminately. Ducks Unlimited has gone to the expense of publishing a bulletin on hawks. It concludes with this statement: "Unless any of them [hawks] are doing harm to you—let them go their way in peace. They have their place in Nature and have their appeal to all those who appreciate beauty and adaption to their mode of life. Do not allow your sympathies for their prey to turn your heart and hand against them. There is more in this Predator-Prey relationship than meets the eye. Dame Nature fitted them for their role and she is a wise old Dame and knows what she is doing. Don't forget that you, Mr. Man, are the greatest predator of them all, and a wanton destroyer if ever there was one."

Perhaps the earliest significant effort to educate the public about the value of birds of prey was the publication in 1893 of *The Hawks and Owls of the United States in Their Relation to Agriculture* by Dr. A. K. Fisher. It was issued by the U. S. Department of Agriculture and reported the results of studying the stomach contents of 2,690 birds of prey. It concluded that the rodent control activities of the great majority of hawks and owls entitled them to protection at the hands of farmers and others.

It has been pointed out that one pair of meadow mice could be responsible for one million relatives within a year's time if their fecundity was not disturbed. Some 23 million pounds of vegetable matter would be needed to feed this bustling family for one year!

Nature has provided controls for the mouse population. Not only the birds of prey, but a wide variety of mammals, eat mice as a staple food.

Biologists have been reiterating for years that availability is the major factor in determining what predators eat. Because there are many more insects and rodents than any other food, it is not surprising that studies show these items to be basic in the diet of most birds of prey. A surprising amount of predation on game birds and songirds, as well as other creatures, is upon what biologists call "surplus populations"—individuals that cannot be supported by the environment and which in most instances would perish whether eaten by the flesh-eaters or not. It is clear to biologists, but often not so to the hunters to whom they preach, that a game bird or mammal taken by a predator does not ordinarily mean that there will be one less of that species in the game bag the following fall. The web of life in the out-of-doors is such a complicated one that biology rather than mathematics must be relied upon.

In the early days of educational efforts on behalf of the hawks and owls, major emphasis was placed on the stomach contents of these birds. This was apparent not only in A. K. Fisher's *Hawks and Owls of North America* (1893) but as recently as John B. May's *Hawks of North America* (1935). If a species was fortunate enough to consume largely insect and small mammal food, it was dubbed "beneficial." A considerable amount of game or poultry remains put the species into the "harmful" category. While these classifications were undoubtedly useful at the time, it had to be assumed that the man with a gun could and would learn to distinguish one species of raptor from another. Unfortunately that was not the case, and it is true even today that, generally speaking, the only persons who can distinguish among the various hawks and owls are those who would not shoot them anyway.

Among a small but influential segment of the population, the idea of there being "harmful" and "beneficial" raptores was rather widely accepted and now we face the difficult task of "undoing" that job in the light of ecological knowledge that makes such distinctions unsound.

One of the leading conservation philosophers of our day, Dr. Irston Barnes, President of the Audubon Society of the District of Columbia, expresses his views on this subject of man's ethics and nature's laws in a most convincing way: "In the world of nature," he says, "there are no good and bad birds. Each animal is chained by countless centuries of evolution to an instinctive pattern of behavior, the most basic of which pertains to the food it eats and the manner of its capture. Thus a hawk is powerless to alter its tastes or its manners. This dictate of nature assures that each form of life shall fulfill its destiny, that no chaos of individual choices shall destroy nature's balance of resources, and that no essential job shall be left undone. The very fact that a form of life exists is clear testimony to its rightness; each form has its essential role in a healthy wildlife community."

We seem to insist upon and delight in imposing our human moral standards upon wildlife. As Paul L. Errington has so aptly put it, "It is unfortunate that man, the specialist in evil, sees in predation among wild animals so much evil that isn't there."

It is wrong for a man to kill a man; therefore, we reason, it must be wrong for a bird to kill a bird. We fail to recognize that civilized man, through his thinking powers, has freed himself from the need for going out and personally killing his own animal food. His substitute system is the breeding of beef cattle, the slaughterhouse, and the meat market.

We cannot expect Song Sparrows to match our human system— to breed insects systematically for their food! They must hunt, kill and eat their insect food where they can find it. If the natural enemies of Song Sparrows, such as Sharp-shinned Hawks, are reduced or eliminated, there may be too many sparrows competing for a limited food supply. Nature's controls, other than predators, are starvation and disease. Doesn't this indicate that we should look with understanding eyes upon the woodland drama in which a Sharp-shinned Hawk captures a Song Sparrow in flight and snuffs out its life in an instant? Would it be more humane for the sparrow to meet slow death by starvation?

Hunters and farmers are not the only persecutors of the birds of prey. There are the "bird lovers" who put out feeding stations and proceed cheerfully to commit mayhem on the "bad" birds that are attracted. These persons see joy in the face of a Chickadee and evil in the visage of a Sharp-shinned Hawk. They apparently feel the Creator slipped up a bit when He gave us jays, hawks, and owls, so they are out to remold the wildlife community after their own design. The distinguished ornithologist and artist, George Miksch Sutton, probably had that philosophy in mind when he wrote in *The Auk*, "The public must be brought to a realization of the fact that great beauty is to be found where mere prettiness does not exist, that the soaring of the wide-winged hawks, their discordant cries, their mottled plumage and gleaming eyes, are just as truly beautiful as the fluttering flight, cheerful songs, and sweet faces of our smaller bird neighbors. Surely, an appreciation of the beauty and majesty of these birds of prey does not demand a special spiritual endowment of some sort! Our deepest, most sincere reasons for protecting wildlife are not, after all, based on economic values. If we can make the public sense the need for these magnificent creatures in everyone's experience, the preservation of the birds of prey which are now too rare will become an important and fascinating feature of the wildlife conservation movement."

Because public sentiment usually lags considerably behind scientific research, it is not surprising that legal protection for the birds of prey has been slow in coming. Hawks, owls, eagles, and vultures were omitted when most birds were extended protection by the Migratory Bird Treaty between Great Britain and the United

States in 1918 and also in the Convention with Mexico in 1936. However, all but seven states have enacted laws which protect at least some of the hawks, owls, and eagles. Most states exempt the Accipiters or so-called "bird hawks" from protection. This has resulted in very little attempt at enforcing the laws. A violator brought into court simply pleads that he thought he was shooting an unprotected hawk. Usually the case is dropped.

Recognition of the weaknesses of present legislation and a more general appreciation of the role of even the "bird hawks" in the general ecology of the outdoors has resulted in the development of considerable sentiment for protection of all hawks and owls. So far only three states have taken this bold step—Connecticut, Michigan, and Indiana—but others are pondering it. A clause in such legislation, permitting the taking of protected birds by the farmer on his own property when such birds are in the act of doing actual damage, protects the landowner who may suffer from the depredations of those few individual hawks which develop a taste for poultry.

It is generally recognized that a high percentage of North American hawks from widely scattered areas are funneled into fairly narrow flight lanes during migrations. Thus, wholesale slaughter of hawks at vantage points along the flyways can nullify much of the protection these birds receive on their breeding grounds. For example, certain of the hawks protected by law in Connecticut during the summer can legally be shot in each state through which they migrate in fall and spring.

To lessen extensive killing of hawks during migration and to compensate in part for the failure to protect them under the Migratory Bird Treaties, some conservationists are advocating that all hawks be protected during migrations (September 1 to November 30, and March 1 to April 30) by an Act of Congress. This would be comparable to the federal statute which protects the Bald Eagle at all times. Except during migrations, hawks would continue to be under the jurisdiction of state laws. It is believed that such legislation would not create the volume of opposition that might be expected if it were proposed to protect by federal law all hawks at all times.

Despite the fact that a great many valiant defenders of the birds of prey have come forward and are doing an outstanding educational job, ignorance about these birds and persecution of them is still widespread. There are, though, many reasons to be encouraged. The tremendous growth of public interest in bird watching as a hobby means that large numbers of people are afield actively observing the birds of prey. In many cases these people go into areas where hawk shooters formerly mowed down their victims during migration. The shooters feel guilty to operate when bird watchers are around, perhaps because many of the shooters realize that they are violating state laws.

Discovery of a hawk slaughtering ground on a lookout in the Kittatinny Mountains of Pennsylvania led to the establishment in 1934 of the Hawk Mountain Sanctuary, near Allentown, where once shooters killed and maimed hundreds of hawks and eagles every week end during migration. Now bird watchers flock to the Sanctuary to observe the impressive spectacle of southward bound hawks and eagles. On a banner day thousands of birds of prey may be observed from the lookout. The early hostility of the nearby residents has turned into open friendliness as a stream of tourists from all over the continent has come to Hawk Mountain—some 12,000 visitors a year. An absorbing account of the history and functions of the sanctuary is contained in the book *Hawks Aloft* by Maurice Broun.

Other famous hawk-watching locations are Cape May in New Jersey, where the slaughter continues despite determined efforts to stop it, and Duluth, Minnesota, where great numbers of hawks swing down the north shore of Lake Superior and come right over the city. The shooting which once took place even in city parks has now been virtually stamped out by the educational and enforcement work of the Duluth Bird Club, an active branch of the National Audubon Society. Unfortunately, there are still many places where such progress has not been made.

There can be do doubt that the tide is turning in favor of the birds of prey. Bishop Robert Hatch of Connecticut, who admits that he once classified all hawks as "big chicken hawks" or "little chicken hawks" has written an eloquent expression of his "conversion." "To me the hawk is the supreme expression of the amazing orchestra of nature, from which no note can be subtracted without serious consequence to man himself. Hawks are an integral part of that orchestra, as well as an expression of its vast score of checks and balances. They are important to us. When we destroy them through ignorance or sentimentality we release an army of other creatures, like rodents and insects, which was never meant to be released. It would be crass, however, to think of them only in terms of economics. Far more significant are their beauty, their expression of wildness in an age which has lost touch with the things of the earth, and the fact that they are symbols of the whole architecture of God's created world."

If you enjoy the birds of prey and feel sympathy for their plight, you have a job cut out for you—and it is a "grass roots" educational job. Enlist the interest of your friends and neighbors in better protection for the raptores and try to see to it that the facts and viewpoints presented in this book are spread widely in schools, youth groups, and farmers' and sportsmen's organizations. The future of the birds of prey is in your hands.

NOTE: The decision arrived at by the American Ornithologists' Union meeting of 1954 at Madison, Wisconsin, to discontinue the use of common names in designating subspecies, came too late for compliance therewith in this volume. The nomenclature used therefore, follows that of former and longstanding procedure.

A. S., JR.

# HAWKS

ORDER *Falconiformes*

# 1. The Vultures

FAMILY *Cathartidae*

North American Vultures are large dark-plumaged birds with small bare heads; rather large but weak feet, without definite talons. The food is largely carrion, though living prey is occasionally taken, particularly by one species (Black Vulture).

## TURKEY VULTURE

*Cathartes aura septentrionalis* Wied
(Gr., *kathartes*, purifier; So. Am., *aura*, name for the bird; Lat., *septentrionalis*, northern)

LOCAL NAMES: Buzzard, Turkey Buzzard, Red-headed Buzzard.

RECOGNITION: Head naked, skin dull to bright red; bill china white midway to tip, red basally; plumage dark rusty brown, feather tips lighter brown. Under surface of wings grayish *from primaries to body* along trailing edge. Legs and feet flesh-colored.
   Length: 26 to 32 inches; wingspread 68 to 72 inches.

NESTING: Usually on the ground, under fallen logs or tangles of vines, hollows, caves, or bare cliff ledges. Elevated nests seldom encountered.
   Eggs: 2, occasionally 3. Dull or creamy white, variously marked with brown, black, or lavendar spots and splashes. Measurement 2.70×1.85 inches.

RANGE: From southern British Columbia through the Prairie Provinces to southern Ontario, central New York, and New England, south to Lower California, northern Mexico, and the Gulf Coast to the Atlantic. Winters throughout regular Atlantic slope range, but rarely north of Ohio Valley, Nebraska, and California. Occurs casually north to Newfoundland. (The Mexican Turkey Vulture, *cathartes aura aura* Linnaeus, a tropical race of Panama, Cuba and Mexico, occurs at times in southern Texas and Florida.)

HISTORY. This species is the most widespread of the family, occurring from the Atlantic to the Pacific and from Canada to Mexico and southward. The all but universal name of buzzard applied to it is erroneous, for true buzzards are actually hawks. Nevertheless, the term is so firmly rooted that it will probably never be supplanted.

The Turkey Vulture occurs in nearly all habitats except heavy forests. Mountains, plains, deserts, and seacoasts are all the same to it, for a dead deer in open northern woodlands, a jack rabbit on the western deserts, or a stranded catfish on a southern sea beach are all carrion and therefore acceptable food for this bird.

Because of their unattractive diet, vultures are widely regarded with distaste, but a moment's reflection should be enough to make us thankful that such birds exist. Indeed, in tropical and subtropical countries the disposal of decomposing animal matter has a direct correlation with good health, and without the presence and activity of vultures, disease would undoubtedly be far more prevalent in those regions.

These sombers birds are virtually dooryard, or at least street, residents in many southern sections of the continent, and prior to the days of efficient garbage disposal were common in some southeastern cities of this country. Though not always listed in the "protected" category, they have long been subjects of unwritten law and are rarely molested by people living where vultures are common.

Vultures are often late risers, sitting about the roost until the sun is well up and spreading their wings to catch and retain its early rays. Ugly, clumsy, and awkward as they are on the ground, or perched, the transformation which takes place when they are in the air is remarkable. Aloft, they are the epitome of avian grace, and their mastery of air currents, thermals, and cross winds is a never-ending source of wonder. When soaring on a rising current, the birds appear independent of the earth, without a movement of the wide pinions to keep them aloft.

The long controversy continues as to the comparative importance to these birds of sight and smell in locating food. Numerous experiments have been made in this regard with contradictory results. However, it now seems generally agreed that both senses are employed, with sight predominating. As with all birds, efficiency of vision far exceeds that of man.

In soaring there is a distinct dihedral (V) in the position of the wings, a characteristic which will separate the vulture from the eagle, the latter's wings being perfectly flat across.

Actually, the flight is much the best means of separating the two species of vultures and has, in my opinion, been subordinated in the literature of ornithology to less readily recognizable factors. The Turkey Vulture flies with rather slow, deep, deliberate beats, the Black Vulture with rapid ones which give the impression of laboring heavily. By this single means—though of course there are others—it is easily possible to determine identity from as far as the eye can see. The Turkey Vulture also veers and tilts in its flight to a far greater degree than the Black, which hardly indulges in such behavior at all.

It is unusual for this species to take living prey, and when it does so, the victims are such helpless creatures as small snakes and newly hatched young herons and ibises. Its value as a scavenger should not be questioned and protection should be afforded it officially, as well as by unwritten law, in every state. Accusations have been brought against it at times as a carrier and spreader of domestic stock disease, but detailed investigations have failed to show any basis in fact for the charges.

The vultures are as nearly voiceless as a bird can be. A hiss, or low grunt, seems to be the limit of vocal attainment, and these are heard mainly when the birds are in competition over a carcass.


# BLACK VULTURE

*Coragyps atrata* (Meyer)
(Gr., *coragyps,* a raven-vulture; Lat., *atrata,* black)

LOCAL NAMES: Black Buzzard, Buzzard, Carrion Crow, Charleston Buzzard, Black-headed Buzzard.

RECOGNITION: Entire plumage dull black; head bare and black; bill dark at base, light at tip; legs light grayish. Large whitish patches at ends of wings on under surface, *very conspicuous in flight.*
Length: 23 to 27 inches; wingspread 54 to 60 inches.

NESTING: Either on the ground or in hollow stumps above or below ground level; in the edges of thick scrub palmetto clumps; occasionally in cavities of rocks and boulders of mountain areas.

Eggs: 2, occasionally 1, rarely 3. Pale gray-green or bluish-white, usually wreathed about the large end with markings of dark brown and purple, or with such spots distributed over the whole egg. Average measurement 3.00 × 2.00 inches.

RANGE: From central Texas, Kansas, southern Illinois, Indiana, and Virginia south through the southern states to Mexico and Central America. Accidental north of Virginia and Maryland.


HISTORY. Largely a southeastern and tropical bird, the Black Vulture occupies in this country only about a quarter of the range that the Turkey Vulture frequents. It is well-named black, the entire plumage and bare head being of a dull, sooty hue. Smaller than the Turkey Vulture by some nine inches, the Black Vulture often associates with it and the two are frequently seen on the same carcass. Either on the ground or in the air, there need never be the slightest doubt as to which is which. The following comparisons will serve to show why:

The Turkey is a definitely brownish bird; the Black is dull, sooty black.

The Turkey flies with slow wing beats, the Black with very rapid ones.

The Turkey has a long, rounded tail, the Black a short, square tail.

The Turkey has a red head; the Black has a black one.

The Turkey shows light areas under the wing from body to tip, the Black only at the tips.

The Turkey's wings are held in a definite V when soaring, those of the Black nearly horizontal.

Though a carrion feeder, the Black Vulture is more predaceous than the Turkey. This tendency to predation may or may not be a localized habit, but it definitely exists, much having been learned about it in recent years. There is, and long has been, undoubted predation by vultures in the Heron-Ibis rookeries of the Southeast and Gulf Coasts, upon both eggs and young. There are outbreaks, at times, of attack on newly born calves on the great cattle ranches of south central Florida and Texas. I have watched this in Florida, and the method of attack has been recorded on motion-picture film. Such attack extends to small pigs and lambs in varying localities. Lack of carrion in localized areas may well be the basis for attacks on living prey. Predation on poultry or game birds is practically nil. I have never witnessed it nor have I talked to anyone who has, though instances of it have been recorded in the literature (*Oologist*, 1909, pp. 191-93).

Accusations of spreading hog cholera have been directed against both vultures, but this has never been definitely proved. Many a vulture has fallen victim to trapping and poisoning campaigns, probably without justification.

It seems certain, however, that the Black Vulture's economic importance in its natural choice of carrion outweighs occasional damage done in a local sense against domestic stock. Such an evaluation may be difficult for an individual rancher to assimilate or sympathize with, but the tendency to look at a continental picture through backyard eyes is one of the great deterrents to sound conservation practices. Except in isolated cases where specific control appears necessary, the Black Vulture should be protected throughout its range.

# CALIFORNIA CONDOR

*Gymnogyps californianus* (Shaw)
(Lat., *Gymnogyps*, naked, vulture; *californianus*, of California)

LOCAL NAME: California Vulture.

RECOGNITION: Largest of North American land birds.
Adult: Head and neck bare, skin yellow, orange, or red; bill whitish; body plumage sooty black, with upper wing coverts and secondaries edged with whitish, axillars and under wing coverts pure white; ruff or collar of pointed feathers at base of neck.
Immature: Neck covered with grayish-sooty down; bill and naked head blackish; upper parts present scaled effect because of brownish edging of feathers; white underwings lacking.
Length: 43 to 55 inches; wingspread 8.5 to 11 feet.

NESTING: In caves of cliffs, egg being laid on bare rock. Apparently does not breed every year.
Eggs: 1, greenish or bluish-white, unmarked. Measurement 4.45 × 1.55 inches.

RANGE: Former: California west of the Great Basin and deserts into northwestern Lower California, from Tehama County south along western slope of the Sierra Nevada and through the Coast Ranges from Humboldt County to the Mexican line. Occasionally occurred in Oregon and Washington and eastward to southern Utah.
Present: Portions of a few counties of southwestern California.

HISTORY. Though now so rare as to be out of the picture in an economic sense, this largest of American land birds once occupied an extensive western range. Its present number totals about sixty individual birds, confined to small mountain areas of southern California.

The immense size, tremendous wingspread, and imposing appearance of the Condor in its natural haunts leaves an unforgettable picture in the mind of the fortunate observer. On the ground the bird exhibits the characteristic vulturine awkwardness, but in flight is transformed into a spectacle of magnificence unmatched by any species.

The food is almost entirely carrion, but instances of predation among small animals, wild and domestic, are on record. Every effort is being made currently to conserve and build up the slim population of the Condor, the National Audubon Society and other organizations being determined that it shall not vanish from earth and sky.

This giant bird is a dweller of open, largely treeless country— high mountain plateaus, canyons, and desert. Over them it soars on ten-foot wings searching the terrain for dead animal life, or perches on bare crags in hunched immobility. The area it now frequents in the Los Padres National Forest is an inviolate sanctuary, and co-operative efforts of federal agencies and conservation organizations are doing as much as possible to save it. Few present-day bird watchers have been privileged to see a Condor, but if such an opportunity comes their way it is a memorable one. My only view of it was one afternoon in the canyon country out of Fillmore when five of the huge creatures, one of them very close, soared overhead. A Golden Eagle, happening to pass a few minutes later, was so dwarfed by comparison as to seem almost insignificant.

The intermittent nature of the Condor's nesting habits, the fact that but one egg is laid and that the youngster is in the nest for many months, all combine to make any population increase a slow process. The bird deserts the nest upon slight provocation, so that strict measures are necessary to keep anxious photographers from disturbing it. One of the factors that formerly militated against its increase was the desire of collectors to obtain the egg, which naturally possessed high value in cash or exchange.

Though the Turkey Vulture and Golden Eagle occur in the same area, the field differences between them and the Condor are easily apparent. The latter's size is at once diagnostic, and the great amount of white on the undersurface of the wings and ruff of feathers about the base of the neck distinguish it from the lesser Vulture. The bare head plus the white of the wings separate it from the Eagle.

Bird students interested in detailed knowledge of the Condor will find a mine of information in *The California Condor,* Research Report No. 4, by Carl Koford (N.Y., National Audubon Society, 1953).

# 11. The Kites

## FAMILY *Accipitriidae*

These small or medium-sized "hawklike" Raptores are characterized by graceful, airy flight on long, narrow wings, hovering when sighting prey then dropping with dangling legs and upraised wings, or taking prey on the wing and devouring it in the air. One species, the Everglade Kite, varies in having broad wings like a Buteo, and eating only snails; other kites are insectivorous in diet.

## WHITE-TAILED KITE

*Elanus leucurus majusculus* Bangs and Penard
(Lat., *elanus*, a kite; Gr., *leucurus*, white-tailed; Lat., *majusculus*, somewhat greater)

LOCAL NAMES: White Hawk, Black-winged Kite.

RECOGNITION: Adult: Upper parts pale bluish-gray, fading to white on head; underparts white; black line over eye; upper wing coverts black, forming a conspicuous dark area at bend of wing; tail square or very slightly notched, white; feet yellow.

Immature: Crown cinnamon; back streaked with brownish; breast and underparts streaked with reddish; forehead and throat white; tail gray with dark subterminal band and white tip.

Length: 15 to 17 inches; wingspread about 40 inches.

NESTING: Usually in oaks or maples, sometimes sycamores, from 18 to 50 feet; of sticks, twigs lined with grasses, rootlets, and moss. Occasionally return to old nest and add to it.

Eggs: 4 to 5. Described by Bent (1937) as "among the most beautiful and richly colored of any of the hawks' eggs." White or cream-white, splashed, marbled, and spotted with varying shades of brown, sometimes in a wreath about the large end. Measurement 1.65 × 1.25 inches.

RANGE: California west of the deserts, from the upper Sacramento Valley and Humboldt County south to the San Diego area and northern Lower California. Also Texas to Lower Rio Grande Valley, Oklahoma, South Carolina, and Florida (rarely), south to Guatemala. Accidental in Louisiana, Illinois, and Michigan.

HISTORY. In a group notable for grace and beauty, the White-tailed Kite occupies a high place. It is, in the bird-watcher's language, unforgettable. Lack of fear of man seems inherent in all of the American kites, much to their undoing in the past. The White-tail is no exception and has been sadly depleted in numbers as a result of ignorance based on unreasoning prejudice.

Never abundant, the range of this kite showed large gaps even in former years, but in very recent times there seems to have been something of a "comeback" in areas once frequented and from which it was all but eliminated. May, for instance (1935), gives in his "Range" a quote from A. C. Bent to the effect that it had been extirpated from Florida. There have been several authentic sight records of it there in the past two or three years, indicating a slight increase at any rate. I have never seen this kite either in South Carolina, my home state, or in Florida, but have had experience with it in southern Texas and the Sacramento Valley of California as well as elsewhere in the latter state. The bird instills admiration in everyone who sees it. Truly, it is a lovely bit of animated, airy grace.

Seen at any distance, the *whiteness* of the bird is striking. A gull or white pigeon comes to mind almost automatically. Closer observation will, of course, reveal the black shoulders and, often the habit of dangling the legs will be diagnostic as will be the manner of hovering flight in which the wings are half raised over the body with the tips (primaries) curving downward. Coursing over a field or meadow, rising, falling, hovering, then plummeting into the grass for prey, it imparts a sense of thrilling admiration to the watcher and constitutes a memorable sight.

Though not a great many stomach examinations of this kite have been made, those on record point to one pattern. Its diet consists of such prey as mice, rats, grasshoppers, beetles, and crickets. Of six stomachs analyzed, five contained remains of small mammals and one was empty. Over a hundred years ago, Audubon wrote of this kite that he had found remains of birds in a few he examined. A. K. Fisher, one of the most eminent authorities in the twentieth century on the food of the birds of prey, says that this is "an experience no naturalist has shared with him [Audubon] as far as I know."

How then, other than by unreasoning prejudice, could the notion arise that this little kite preys upon quail, ducks, and other game birds? Because of such belief, however, the kite has been shot by hunters, gamekeepers, and the general public. The kite looks and acts like a hawk, and therefore is marked as an enemy.

The White-tailed Kite deserves protection by everyone interested in the preservation of beauty and the stability of natural resources.


## SWALLOW-TAILED KITE

*Elanoides forficatus forficatus* (Linnaeus)
(Gr. and Lat., *elanoides*, like a kite; Lat., *forficatus*, fork-tailed)

LOCAL NAMES: Fork-tailed Kite, Wasp Hawk, Fork-tailed Hawk.

RECOGNITION: Adult: Head, neck, rump, and underparts white; back, wings, and tail black, glossed with purplish. Wings long and narrow; tail deeply forked, outer feathers about eight inches longer than the others.

Immature: Similar to adult but with whitish tips to many of the black feathers and narrow blackish streaks on the white body feathers.

Length: 19 to 25.5 inches; wingspread 45 to 50 inches.

NESTING: Usually in pines or cypresses at considerable heights, 75 to 130 feet. Composed of sticks and twigs with a lining of Spanish moss and feathers. Often in a crotch or a branch of small dimensions. (One nest has been recorded at a height of over 200 feet in a cottonwood tree in Texas).

Eggs: usually 2, sometimes 3 or 4. Creamy white, boldly and irregularly splashed, spotted and blotched with various shades of brown and lavender. Measurement 1.80×1.50 inches.

RANGE: Formerly bred locally from northern Minnesota, southern Wisconsin and Indiana, North and South Carolina, to Florida, Alabama, and eastern Mexico. Now restricted from about lower South Carolina to parts of Florida. Winters in the tropics south of the United States. Accidental in the area west of the 100th meridian, southern Canada, and the northern and northeastern states.

HISTORY. Everything that might be said of the kite family in the way of praise is summed up and reflected by this elegant species. Many consider it the most beautiful bird in the country, not because of striking color, for it possesses only that ever compelling combination of black and white, but because it is the very essence of aerial grace and streamlined symmetry. Vulture, Albatross, Frigate Bird, and Falcon have all seemed the ultimate to some, but without further comparison the Swallow-tailed Kite soars alone.

Over cypress swamp and mangrove coast, open field or prairie edge, it sails with straightaway, arrowy ease; it banks, turns, towers, and sideslips to swoop within inches of the earth in seizing grasshopper or snake, then slants aloft to consume its victim in the air. Black and white against the blue, wings and deeply cleft tail etched sharply in living silhouette, it need not, as Bent has well said, "be mistaken for anything else." It is an unforgettable bird.

May (1935) quotes a fine description of this bird by Elliott Coues:

. . . marked among its kind by no ordinary beauty of form and brilliancy of color, the Kite courses through the air with a grace and buoyancy it would be vain to rival. By a stroke of the thin-bladed wings and a lashing of the cleft tail, its flight is swayed to this or that side in a moment, or instantly arrested. Now it swoops with incredible swiftness, seizes without a pause, and bears its struggling captive aloft, feeding from its talons as it flies; now it mounts in airy circles till it is a speck in the blue ether and disappears. One cannot watch the flight of the Kite without comparing it with the thoroughbred racer.

The food habits of the Swallow-tail are much the same as those of its relatives (always excepting the Everglade Kite). Insects predominate and such often destructive forms as grasshoppers, beetles, and crickets are included in its diet. Frogs, lizards, small snakes, and at times mice, according to Simmons (1925) in Texas, are eaten. Fisher (1893) on the other hand, states that it "never molests small birds and mammals." May (1935) gives a summary of thirty stomachs examined, every one of which contained insects. The only other material listed was "vertebrates" other than birds and mammals.

Like the other kites, the Swallow-tail does not occur in sufficient numbers today to be a definite economic factor. It is a part, however, of the intricate system of natural controls which it is important to maintain. Therefore, protection of its remaining population and definite effort toward increasing and maintaining the species are highly desirable. Further, if any bird in the country deserves protection from an aesthetic standpoint, this kite stands at the top of the list. Conservation and sportsmen's groups—to say nothing of the various states fortunate enough to include it in their avifauna—should throw their efforts toward its better welfare.

## MISSISSIPPI KITE

*Ictinia mississippiensis* (Wilson)
(Gr., *Ictinia*, a kite; Lat., *mississippiensis*, of Mississippi)

LOCAL NAMES: Blue Kite, Mosquito Hawk.

RECOGNITION: Adult: General plumage bluish-gray, shoulders and primaries darker; head, neck, and secondary feathers light gray, appearing almost white in some lights; tail black, either square at end or slightly notched. Iris red; feet reddish-orange.

Immature: More or less streaked on upperparts, with black and white;

underparts with spots of reddish-brown and buff; tail and wing quills black, tipped with white.

Length: 13 to 17 inches; wingspread 35 to 37 inches.

NESTING: Widely variable in elevation, at times no more than 10 or 12 feet and sometimes as much as 135 feet. Compact and well made of sticks and twigs, lined with green leaves, sometimes moss. Nest depression very shallow.

Eggs: 1 or 2. Pale bluish-white, unmarked. Measurement 1.65 × 1.25 inches.

RANGE: Formerly bred from northeastern Kansas, southern Illinois, Indiana, and South Carolina south to Texas and Florida. Now nests locally in Kansas, Oklahoma, Tennessee, South Carolina, and the Gulf States. Winters from southern Florida and Texas southward through Mexico to Central America. Accidental elsewhere.

HISTORY. In common with many other American birds, this kite bears a misleading name. Geographical terms are unfortunate in connection with birds in most cases. The present species is no more essentially Mississippian than the Florida Gallinule is of that state, or the Louisiana Heron of its place name. Black-tailed Kite would have been both descriptive and appropriate, for this character is one of its best field marks.

Like the other three kites, this one has been much reduced in numbers since the turn of the century and has disappeared from a great part of its former range. However, in certain areas one may still find it in localized numbers, and it shows a marked tendency to return to a rather restricted locality year after year. Oklahoma, Texas, western Florida (panhandle), and coastal South Carolina are reasonably certain to contain small populations.

Its mastery of flight, grace, and remarkable evolutions compare favorably with both the White and Swallow-tailed Kites, but it seems inclined to ascend to greater heights and soar in huge circles for long periods, so far aloft, indeed, that it all but disappears from the unaided human vision. At times it dives with breath-taking speed, swoops, zigzags, and banks in astonishing acrobatics. A characteristic maneuver is that of turning over and over in somersaults like a tumbler pigeon.

Seen in the sky, as is usual, the square black tail is easy proof of its identity, together with the light gray head, which often appears white at some distance. Its similarity to a giant swallow is very marked.

This kite takes prey on the wing and devours it in the air, seeming to be independent of the earth much of the time. The food of the Blue Kite, as it is sometimes called, is largely similar to the family preference, with a predilection toward large insects. Grasshoppers, locusts, cicadas, katydids, large beetles, and dragonflies are consistently taken. Small snakes, lizards, and frogs vary such diet, but all authorities agree that this kite never preys on birds. Indeed, many observers have noted that small birds pay no attention to it even in close proximity.

Bent (1937) quotes Stephens in Oklahoma, to the effect that remains of toads, mice, and young rabbits have been found in the kite's nest before the young have left.

Every farmer should welcome the presence of this attractive courser of woods and fields about his acres, and yet prejudice arising from ignorance has caused wide diminution of a valuable avian asset. The deplorable and erroneous adage that the "only good hawk is a dead one" has caused untold loss.


## EVERGLADE KITE

*Rostrhamus sociabilis plumbeus* (Ridgway)
(Lat., *rostrhamus*, hooked bill; *sociabilis*, sociable; *plumbeus*, lead-colored)

LOCAL NAME: Snail Hawk.

RECOGNITION: Adult male: Uniformly dark slate, almost black, head and back slightly lighter. Basal portion of tail and tail coverts white. Bill very slender and strongly hooked, black; cere, lores, and legs bright red.

Adult female: Upperparts rusty black; underparts streaked and mottled with brownish and buff; whitish patches on sides of head.

Immature: Like the female but with a brighter shade of brown, streakings of brown, yellowish, and white; tail as in adults.

Length: 16 to 18 inches; wingspread about 45 inches.

NESTING: A bulky, rather shallow structure of grasses, weeds, and small sticks, lined with grass. Attached to stems of cattails or sawgrass, or placed in willows or other aquatic growth from 1 foot to 6 or 8 feet above water.

Eggs: 4, sometimes fewer. Whitish, profusely marked with splashes and spots of various shades of brown and cinnamon. Much variation occurs. Very light eggs sometimes found. Measurement 1.75 × 1.50 inches.

RANGE: Peninsular Florida south to Cuba, eastern Mexico, and Central America. Now restricted largely to Lake Okeechobee and adjacent fresh water marshes in this country.

HISTORY. So completely at variance with other kites is this species in appearance, behavior, and diet that it is difficult to think of them as relatives. This species is the most highly specialized bird in America and, for that reason if no other, deserves a continued place among our avian forms. Actually, it vies with the California Condor in being the third rarest bird in the United States, occupying about the same population status. (The Ivory-billed Woodpecker is rarest, with the Whooping Crane in second place.)

Not only in habit and food preference does it differ from other birds of prey, but in range also. It was formerly a dweller in almost any extensive fresh water marsh of Florida (peninsular), but is now confined to the southwest corner of Lake Okeechobee and a few isolated spots of the Kissimmee River valley and eastern Everglades (Loxahatchee). Strays may now and then occur elsewhere, but are only wandering individuals.

No one who has seen and watched this bird will forget it. Despite the unparalleled grace of the Swallow-tail, the fragile beauty of the White-tail, and the aerial performances of the Mississippi, the sight of this wide-winged cruiser of the sawgrass produces a thrill all its own.

Much more like the Buteo hawks than its own cousins, the broad wings, white tail patch, and brilliant red feet are striking characteristics of this kite. At a distance it markedly resembles the Marsh Hawk and is often confused with the latter, even by guides who are familiar with both birds. There are, of course, definite differences in the Everglade Kite—the wider wings, white tail patch instead of white rump, and the horizontal instead of veering, tilting flight of the Harrier.

The Everglade Kite never seems in a hurry. It is a deliberate bird, never flustered or erratic. With deep strokes of the wings it slowly searches the water beneath, peering keenly downward, then swings around and covers another sector. When prey is sighted, the bird towers slightly, hovers, then drops downward with dangling legs, seizes the prey in its talons, usually transfers it to the beak, and flaps off to a nearby perch. The same perch is returned to time and again—perhaps an old stake in the marsh, perhaps a mound of aquatic debris or a cattail clump. About the base of the perch are abundant evidences of the cast-off portions of its only food. It is this food that really stamps the species as a bird apart, for its limitation of choice is its outstanding characteristic. The entire diet consists of *one species of fresh-water snail*. This creature is the Apple or Moon Snail *(Pomacea caliginosus)*, formerly called *Ampullaria depressa*.

The range of this snail once occupied the greater part of peninsular Florida wherever fresh-water marsh occurred, but drainage has much reduced it. The snail extends into southern Georgia, but is not followed there by the kite. This snail is also eaten by the Limpkin, but not exclusively. It places pearly clusters of eggs on the stems of aquatic grasses; these hatch, drop into the water, and grow to a maximum size about that of a child's fist. As far as is known, *Pomacea* is of no importance economically one way or the other. It would seem to follow, then, that the Everglade Kite is in the same category, but it is certainly a most attractive and unique form of avian life and well deserves protective encouragement from that standpoint alone.

The decline in numbers of this interesting species has been based not only on the drainage of marshes and varying water levels, with consequent elimination of its food supply, but also on shooting by thoughtless hunters who follow the old rule that the elimination of a hawk is a meritorious deed. Collectors of birds' eggs and skins have been a factor as well, though such practice is now largely controlled and almost nonexistent. The uninformed duck hunter is now the most dangerous enemy of the Everglade Kite. Sitting in a blind, impatient at the intervals between arrivals of ducks over his decoys, the hunter sees an obvious hawk cruising nearby. It comes within range, he shoots, and the bird crumples to the water. As many as five of these kites have been found floating at one time in front of a single blind on Lake Okeechobee.

Until education can alter the uninformed viewpoint, the immediate future of the Everglade Kite is problematical. However, improvement has already been noted. The State of Florida has become aroused over saving one of its most interesting living assets, and has distributed posters in strategic places asking the co-operation of sportsmen in the preservation of the Snail Hawk. The National Audubon Society, local bird clubs, and federal wildlife agencies are all alive to, and working for, this end. It seems certain that a new day is dawning for the survival of this species, and we can sincerely trust that the awakening has not come too late.

An excellent color film depicting the habitat and behavior of this kite, titled *Phantom of the Marshes*, photographed by Bayard W. Read, may be rented from the National Audubon Society at 1130 Fifth Avenue, New York 28, N.Y.

# III The Accipiters

SUBFAMILY *Accipitriidae*

Three species compose this group, all having short, rounded wings and long tails. Slim-bodied and very fast, they fly with rapid wingbeats and alternate periods of sailing. Their food is largely other birds, which they secure with sudden pounces, appearing and disappearing like phantoms. Their ability at headlong flight through forested growth is phenomenal; in perching they seek secluded resting places amid concealing foliage. Their function in the over-all economy of nature is control of overpopulation. Individuals sometimes create a problem by developing the habit of preying upon domestic fowl.

## AMERICAN GOSHAWKS

### EASTERN GOSHAWK

> *Accipiter gentilis atricapillus* (Wilson)
> (Lat., *Accipiter*, a hawk; *gentilis*, of the clan; *atricapillus*, black-haired)

LOCAL NAMES: Blue Darter, Partridge Hawk, Hen Hawk, Chicken Hawk.

RECOGNITION: Adult: Upperparts dark bluish slate, becoming blackish on crown, whitish on neck; white streak over eye and black line through it; primaries (flight feathers) black with gray bars; underparts white to pearl gray, finely barred with black lines and thin shaft streaks; tail blue-gray narrowly tipped with white and with four dusky bands; iris red; legs and feet yellow.

Immature: Very like a young Cooper's Hawk but with a definitely light streak over the eye.

Length: Male, 20 to 22 inches; female, 22 to 26 inches; wingspread 44 to 47 inches.

NESTING: Usually at rather low elevations in such trees as birch or maple, sometimes evergreens. Made of sticks and twigs, lined with sprigs of pine or fir, with feathers. Often quite bulky. The nest is defended with determined vigor, obliging the human intruder to equip himself with gloves and headnet.

Eggs: 3 to 5. Pale bluish-white, unmarked. Average measurement 2.30 x 1.70 inches.

RANGE: Breeds from northwestern Alaska and Mackenzie, northern Manitoba, Quebec, and Newfoundland south to central British Columbia, Michigan and northern New York, northern New England and Massachusetts, and in mountains to Pennsylvania and western Maryland. Winters from Alaska and southern Canadian Provinces to southern California, northern Mexico, Texas, Oklahoma, Missouri, Kentucky, Illinois, Indiana, northern Ohio, West Virginia, and Virginia. Accidental in Idaho, Arizona, and Florida.

## WESTERN GOSHAWK

*Accipiter atricapillus striatulus* (Ridgway)
(Lat., *striatulus*, streaked)

RECOGNITION: Adult: Dark gray above, darker on crown; underparts finely barred and pencilled, giving impression of uniform blue-gray.

Immature: Brownish-black above; white below with wide black streaks and spots.

RANGE: Breeds in Arctic regions from Cook's Inlet, Alaska, south to the central Sierra Nevada in California (Yosemite), Arizona, New Mexico, and into Old Mexico. Winters through breeding range south to southern California and northern Mexico.

HISTORY. Upon these birds and their relatives, the Sharp-shinned and Cooper's Hawks, much of the hostility attaching to the birds of prey has been built. Many an irate farmer, gamekeeper, or hunter has drawn a bead on a circling, soaring "Chicken Hawk."

and brought it down, while the true culprit has been sitting nearby devouring the hen or quail amid the cover of a tree.

It is true that the Accipiters take birds; that is exactly what they have evolved to do in the wildlife community. Biologically, they are efficient, smooth-working, natural controls on other birdlife which would become too abundant for its own good without check. For fulfilling the purpose for which they were created, man blasts them with malediction and lead. Often forgotten by sportsmen is the fact that there always have been quail, grouse, and ducks *and* hawks. Indeed, in past years there were more game birds and song birds, as well as hawks, than there are now. But man has upset the balance and caused the diminution of all these birds.

The Goshawks are powerful and fearless. Of definitely northern distribution, they are practically unknown in the southern half of the country, but now and then, in severe winter weather, penetrate into and below the middle tier of states. The food of these hawks has been shown by analysis to consist mainly of birds, with a scattering of small mammals. Much of such predation is unseen, for the Accipiters appear like gray phantoms, seize the prey, and vanish as quickly, to devour it amid the sheltering cover of a nearby tree. Their food preference has been vividly illustrated from examinations of some 880 stomachs from various parts of the range of these master hunters. In 496, remains of poultry, game, and other birds were found, and 233 contained mammal remains. At times, the goshawks are marked mammal predators, such prey as rats, mice, lemmings, chipmunks, squirrels, and hares figuring in the take. Only 3 of the 880 stomachs examined contained insects.

The accipitrine hawks are natural controls on mammal and birdlife, but when an individual of this group persists in returning day after day to the same hencoop for easy prey, its elimination may be necessary to save the remaining fowl. The Goshawk is capable of carrying away chickens of nearly its own weight. It sometimes constitutes a definite liability to poultry raisers, and under such conditions should be eliminated by control of the offending individuals, not indiscriminate slaughter.

## SHARP-SHINNED HAWKS

*Accipiter striatus velox* (Wilson)
(Lat., *striatus*, streaked; *velox*, swift or fast)

LOCAL NAMES: Little Blue Darter, Sharpie, Bullet Hawk.

RECOGNITION: Smallest of the Accipiters, sexes alike.

Adult: Upperparts dark blue-gray; underparts white, heavily cross-barred with reddish-brown, throat finely streaked, undertail coverts white; tail square or slightly notched, crossed with three or four narrow bands of dark brown above, grayish-white below.

Immature: Upperparts brownish; underparts white, streaked with blackish.

Length: Male 10 to 12 inches, wingspread 20 to 23 inches; female 12 to 14 inches, spread 24 to 27 inches.

NESTING: Usually in coniferous trees, but at times in cottonwoods and poplars or birch. Made of sticks and twigs rather flat and close to the trunk, from about 20 to 50 feet up.

Eggs: 3 to 5, sometimes up to 7 or 8. Distinctly rounded, white with heavy markings of various shades of brown, in an overlaid effect, at times with vinaceous tints. Among the handsomest of hawk eggs. Occasionally a very lightly marked egg appears in a heavily marked set. Measurement 1.45 × 1.15 inches.

RANGE: Breeds largely throughout the United States and Canada from Alaska and Mackenzie area to Quebec, Labrador, and Newfoundland south to Florida, the Gulf Coast, Texas, Arizona, and west-central California. Winters from Alaska and southern Canada to Guatemala and Panama. Accidental in the Bahamas.

## NORTHWEST COAST SHARP-SHINNED HAWK

*Accipiter striatus perobscurus* Snyder
(Lat., *perobscurus*, very dusky)

RANGE: Islands and mainland from Yakutat Bay, Alaska, to Vancouver Island and southern British Columbia. Winters south to central California.

HISTORY. This little raptor and its larger relative, the Cooper's Hawk, are probably the most persecuted of all the hawks of this continent. The persecution may be explained in several ways:

They are hawks to begin with.

They are widespread in range and still occur in numbers.

They feed largely on other birds.

Everything that might be said of this dashing little predator would apply to the Cooper's Hawk, with increased proportion because of the latter's larger size. The Sharp-shin is too small to capture large poultry and game birds, but it is lightning death to birds of medium sizes and under. Warblers, sparrows, orioles, wrens, robins—all feel the impact of this feathered thunderbolt and seldom see the doom which strikes them. We should remember that it is not vindictive ferocity which drives the killer but hunger, which plays an essential part in the natural economy in the cropping of surpluses. If there were no control there would simply be too many robins, orioles, and warblers to be supported by the available food supply. Curiously enough, some of those hardest to convince of this fact are not sportsmen or hunters in general, but the so-called "bird lovers" who love only those birds that are vegetarians.

The Sharp-shin is a bird hawk and in fairness should be so regarded. An impartial look at the stomach contents of over 1,000 of these little raptores is interesting. Of this number only 64 did *not* contain bird remains.

During migrations these hawks often travel in company and along certain flyways are apt to be seen in considerable numbers. Notable among localities are Point Pelee, Ontario; Hawk Mountain in the Kittitinnys of Pennsylvania; and Cape May, New Jersey. The sexes differ widely in size; the female being definitely larger, a raptorial characteristic. A very large female Sharp-shin will be almost the size of a small male Cooper's Hawk.

Like the other Accipiters, the Sharp-shin is seldom seen in the open but frequents the woods and field edges, where it comes and goes with all the swiftness which its name *velox* implies.

The short, rounded wings are well adapted to flight in forested areas and the Sharp-shin threads its way through thick growth as easily as a wood duck. The small size, heavy streakings, and square tail serve to identify it without much trouble.

May (1935) points out that "The flight of the Sharp-shin is rapid and direct; it is not often seen to circle or soar, and it never poises and hovers with rapidly beating wings as is characteristic of the smaller Falcons. It is often observed dashing into a thicket in headlong pursuit of its feathered prey while consternation reigns among the songbirds. It seldom utters any notes except in the breeding season; when about its nest it sometimes emits 'a high *kee ki ki ki* or a thin whining *whee whee*'; it has also cackling notes suggestive of the Belted Kingfisher, 'flicker-like alarm notes' or a series of short rather shrill screams."

## COOPER'S HAWK

*Accipiter cooperii* (Bonaparte)
(Lat., *cooperi*, for William Cooper)

LOCAL NAMES: Big Blue Darter, Chicken Hawk, Bullet Hawk.

RECOGNITION: A large edition of the Sharp-shin, with a long *rounded* tail.
   Adult: Top of head black; upperparts more blue than the Sharp-shin.
   Immature: Very similar to same in the Sharp-shin; rounded tail is best character.
   Length: Male 14 to 18 inches, wingspread 27 to 30 inches. Female 16.5 to 20 inches, spread 29 to 36 inches.

NESTING: At varying heights, 10 to 50 or 60 feet. Rather bulky, of sticks and twigs, lined with bark; often built upon remains of old hawk or crow nests.
   Eggs: 4 or 5, usually pale bluish-white, unmarked. At times faint markings of light brownish appear, and rarely a well-marked set is found. Measurement 1.90×1.45 inches.

**BLACK VULTURE, TURKEY VULTURE**
Black Vultures at left, Turkey Vultures at right

**CALIFORNIA CONDOR**
Adults at left and in flight, immature perched at right

**WHITE-TAILED KITE**

Adults at left and in flight, immature at right

SWALLOW-TAILED KITE

Adults

**MISSISSIPPI KITE**

Adults

### EVERGLADE KITE
Adult male in foreground, adult female in flight, young male on ground

AMERICAN GOSHAWK

Adult at left, immature at right

**SHARP-SHINNED HAWK**

Adult at right, immature at left

RANGE: Breeds from southern British Columbia across Canada to Prince Edward Island south to Florida, the Gulf Coast and California, and into northern Mexico. Winters from southern British Columbia, Washington, and California across the country to southern New York and New England to Costa Rica.

HISTORY. As mentioned in the description above, this hawk is a large Sharp-shin. General appearance, behavior, and diet are the same, but the rounded tail and size will always help to distinguish the Cooper's Hawk. It is definitely a bird predator and lives primarily on birds the size of robins, quail, meadowlarks, and jays. It sometimes develops a special taste for quail or poultry. Cooper's Hawks are not all chicken eaters, however, since there are reliable accounts of pairs that have nested for years near poultry yards without disturbing the fowl. In the wild, away from the temptations of poultry or pen-reared game, the Cooper's Hawk goes about its age-old task in life—making sure that the numbers of its prey are kept in bounds and that the fittest survive.

The Cooper's Hawk is difficult to control, where necessary, because of its secretive method of hunting and attack, appearing from nowhere and returning thereto as swiftly. A brief glimpse is about as much as one gets of it. Pole traps, so often set for these hawks, are ineffective because this species rarely alights on an open perch. Therefore, the pole trap usually catches species for which it is not intended, and has always been an unmitigated menace to birdlife. It should be completely outlawed everywhere.

No one can deny the inroads upon birdlife inflicted by the accipitrine hawks. It should be kept in mind, though, that they were designed for such practice. Examination of stomach contents of this species parallels that of the Goshawks and the Sharp-shin. Of 422 analyzed, 224 contained bird remains and 129 of the 422 were empty.

This, to some, would be a "shocking" record, but we should guard against too hasty judgment. Man is the greatest killer on earth, not only of those lesser animals over which he has domination, but his own fellow man as well. We might recall the statement made by Paul Errington in the Introduction to this volume, who said that it is "unfortunate that man, the specialist in evil, sees in predation among wild animals so much evil that isn't there."

In describing the bird, May (1935) quotes the following by J. T. Nichols: " 'there is a subtle difference in the character of the flight between the two, that of the Sharp-shin giving the effect of buoyancy and the Cooper's of momentum.' The Cooper's Hawk is likely to be more noisy than the Sharp-shin, its notes including a rather harsh *kluk, kluk, kluk,* a far-reaching *swee-ew* or *psee-ur,* and a shrill *quick, quick, quick,* repeated many times in rapid succession. About its nest 'its metallic *tick, tick, tick* makes identification easy.' "

# IV The Buteos

SUBFAMILY *Buteoninae*

Robust-bodied, broad-tailed birds with round-ended wings, the Buteos are given to perching in open situations or soaring in wide circles in search of prey. Food preferences are largely small mammals, other vertebrates, and insects. Certain species often exhibit melanism (dark-color phases). Although "buzzard" is a term generally applied to the Vultures, it really applies to this family of hawks and they should be so called.

## RED-TAILED HAWKS

### EASTERN RED-TAILED HAWK

> *Buteo jamaicensis borealis* (Gmelin)
> (Lat., *buteo*, a buzzard; *jamaicensis*, of Jamaica; *borealis*, northern)

LOCAL NAMES: Hen Hawk, Rabbit Hawk.

RECOGNITION: Much individual variation.

Adult: Upperparts dark chocolate brown rather mottled with grayish-white; underparts vary from nearly white to brown, but with a broken band of brownish streaking on upper breast and a heavier band across abdomen. Under surface of wings shows dark-tipped feathers. Tail reddish brown with narrow white tip and often a dark subterminal band.

Immature: Upperparts duller brown; underparts whiter; tail like the back, dull brownish crossed by 6 to 10 dark bands. Breast and belly bands less distinct than in adults.

Length: Male 19 to 22.5 inches, wingspread 46 to 50 inches; female 21 to 25 inches, spread 48 to 58 inches.

Melanism: Rare in this form.

NESTING: Either in hardwoods or pines at varying heights from 25 to 50 feet. Same nest occasionally used from year to year and added to. At times abandoned nests of other hawks or owls are used. Well made of sticks and twigs lined with bark strippings and Usnea lichen and moss. Green sprigs utilized at times, renewed during the incubation period.

Eggs: usually 2. Often white or bluish-white, unmarked. At times irregularly spotted or otherwise marked with brownish or purplish, but rarely with any profusion. Measurement 2.35 × 1.80 inches.

RANGE: Breeds from Mackenzie, across Canada to southern Quebec and Newfoundland south to central Texas, northeastern Oklahoma, Alabama, and northern Florida. Winters from Kansas and Iowa across to southern Maine south to northeastern Mexico and the Gulf Coast.


## FLORIDA RED-TAILED HAWK

*Buteo jamaicensis umbrinus* (Bangs)
(Lat., *umbrinus*, dark)


RECOGNITION: Darker above than Eastern Red-tail; throat distinctly streaked; band across lower underparts conspicuous and very dark. Broad blackish band at tip of tail.

Size: Similar to *B. j. borealis*.

RANGE: Peninsular Florida, Cuba, and Isle of Pines. Strays occasionally into southern Georgia and rarely to lower South Carolina.


## KRIDER'S RED-TAILED HAWK

*Buteo jamaicensis krideri* (Hooper)
(Lat., *krideri*, for John Krider)


RECOGNITION: So pale as to appear an albinistic Eastern Red-Tail.

Adult: Upper parts gray-brown with considerable whitish mottling; underparts either entirely white or pale buff, abdominal band sometimes lacking and, if present, much paler than in *B. j. borealis*. Head white; tail pale pinkish or white.

Immature: Tail whitish or light rufous, crossed by 8 to 10 brownish bands, tip white.

Size: Similar to other forms.

RANGE: Breeds from southern Prairie Provinces into Wyoming, North Dakota, and Minnesota south to Missouri and Nebraska. Winters south to Wisconsin, Illinois, Louisiana, and Mississippi. Accidental in lower South Atlantic area.

## WESTERN RED-TAILED HAWK

*Buteo jamaicensis calurus* (Cassin)
(Gr., *calurus*, dock-tailed)

RECOGNITION: Wide variation in individuals, tending strongly toward melanism. More blackish and rufous on underparts, particularly on breast. Tail usually much barred with dark bands. In some specimens entire plumage is sooty brownish black, except for the rufous, dark-banded tail.
Size: Similar to other forms.

RANGE: Breeds from southeastern Alaska and western Mackenzie south to Lower California and east to the edge of Great Plains. Winters from southern British Columbia throughout California to Central America. Casually eastward in migration.

## ALASKA RED-TAILED HAWK

*Buteo jamaicensis alascanus* Grinnell
(Lat., *alascanus*, of Alaska)

RANGE: This form occurs from Yakutat Bay, Alaska, to the Queen Charlotte Islands. It does not differ in habits and behavior from the Western Red-tail.

## FUERTES' RED-TAILED HAWK

*Buteo jamaicensis fuertsi* Sutton and Van Tyne
(Lat., *fuertsi*, for Louis A. Fuertes)

RANGE: This desert form occurs in southwestern Texas, centering somewhat about the region of the Big Bend.

HISTORY. Few hawks have been more misunderstood than these great birds, an example of the "innocent suffering for the guilty."

They are universally known throughout their huge range as Hen Hawk.

To some extent this misnomer is understandable. The Red-tails are soaring hawks, swinging around in great circles which often take them over farm and ranch yards. As they do so, an Accipiter often swoops in from the woodlot or cottonwood grove, seizes a chicken, and vanishes like a wraith. Outcry arises among the remaining poultry, the farmer-rancher rushes out with a shotgun, looks up, sees the soaring Red-tail, aims, fires, and down it comes. With satisfaction he picks up the bird, hangs it on the fence as "scare-hawk," and the incident is closed. And, in ironical aftermath, the successful marauder sits quietly in a tree nearby, making a meal of the chicken.

For days on end the now defunct Red-tail had been patrolling the air over farmyard or ranch. Repeatedly it had ceased its circling and plummeted downward to seize a scurrying rat or crouching rabbit. Rats in the corncrib and feedbins had been steadily diminishing; rabbits in the garden had become fewer of late. Now what happens when the hawk is destroyed? Back come the rats and rabbits; up goes the loss in grain and vegetables. Control has been reduced and the farmer-rancher suffers in consequence. Why? Because he knew that hawks had been taking his chickens, but he did not know that hawks had been keeping the rats, mice, and rabbits down. A hawk was a hawk to the man with a gun—to be killed at sight. That there are different hawks and that they have a varied diet never seems to occur to him. This folly has been repeated now for generations. Every year there are fewer Red-tails and more rodents.

Aside from the westerly distributed Rough-legged Hawks, the Red-tail is the largest of the Buteos. It covers much of North America in one or another of its forms, but is becoming increasingly local. The large size, white underwings and body, black-tipped flight feathers, and dark crossband low down on the abdomen will all help one to know it, but the clinching character is the brick-red tail, easy to see as the bird wheels and banks in aerial turns. The note, once learned, is as good a means to identify the bird as its appearance; the sound is a high, shrill "kree-e-e" uttered on a descending scale.

This interesting description is given by May (1935):

The Red-tailed Hawk is essentially a soaring hawk. It is most often seen (and often heard) sailing high overhead, wheeling in great spirals with wings and tail widely spread, changing its course by merely tilting its tail sideways, and maintaining its lofty elevation with only an occasional stroke of its broad wings. At other times it perches for hours at a time in some commanding situation, usually a dead tree or, in mountainous regions, a ledge. When startled it gets up quickly and with heavy sweeps of its broad pinions rapidly gains momentum and then glides or sails in a spiral course which soon carries it, without apparent change in the relative positions of wings and tail, to a high altitude. It is a noisy bird, especially in the spring of the year.

A brief look at the food habits of this big hawk is illuminating. W. L. McAtee once analyzed 850 Red-tail stomachs from all over the United States; 100 were empty so that actually 750 told the story. Mammal remains were in 650, among which were 385 mice; 86 showed poultry-game bird remains. Thus mammals comprised 86 per cent of the food and birds 12 per cent.

Other examinations concerned 1,013 stomachs, of which 857 held mammals and 112 poultry-gamebirds. Specific prey taken included ground squirrels, rabbits, gophers, rats, mice, prairie dogs, gray and red squirrels, and chipmunks. Chickens, always easy prey and taken largely by immature hawks, plus quail, grouse, and ducks, are taken occasionally. It is well to remember, in this connection, that cripples and even dead birds are eaten now and then, so that it is not correct to assume that such remains found in the stomachs necessarily mean that the hawk in question took healthy or living birds.

It should be obvious that Red-tails are fascinating birds to observe, that they have an important role in the scheme of things, and that their activities definitely further the interests of agricultural production; they are valuable assets. Except when actually seen in the very act of attacking poultry, they should be given every encouragement and complete protection.

# HARLAN'S HAWK

*Buteo harlani* (Audubon)
(Lat., *harlani*, for R. Harlan)

LOCAL NAME: Black Warrior.

RECOGNITION: Upperparts gray-brown to nearly uniform black; underparts varying from white, mottled with dusky to sooty brownish-black. Tail whitish, conspicuously spotted or mottled with dark brown or black. Immature birds show tail barred with dusky.
  Size: About that of the Red-tailed Hawk.

NESTING: Similar to the Red-tail.

RANGE: Breeds from southwestern Yukon and adjacent areas in Alaska and northwestern British Columbia south to southern Alberta. Winters through the Mississippi Flyway to the Gulf Coast, casual or accidental as far west as California and east to South Carolina.

HISTORY. Long thought to be a subspecies of the Red-tailed Hawk, Harlan's is now generally agreed to deserve specific rank. Usually a very dark, all but black bird, it is dichromatic, having a very light phase as well as a dark one. In either phase, however, this hawk can be recognized by the conspicuously mottled or spotted tail. The immature shows dusky crossbars thereon.

Harlan's Hawk was described by Audubon, who was mistaken in his belief that it bred in Louisiana. The nesting range is far to the northwest, reaching into Alaska. It often associates with Red-tails on migration and shares their behavior of flying, at times, at very high altitudes.

Comparatively little is known of the specific food preferences, since few stomachs have been available for study. H. S. Swarth (1926) examined four which held remains of rabbits, ground squirrels, and chipmunks. Collectors in Arkansas (winter range) have reported rabbits and quail in the food, plus rats, mice, and a few small birds. Probably the diet changes to some extent seasonally and geographically. It is doubtless a safe assumption to consider its economic status as similar to that of the Red-tail group.

# RED-SHOULDERED HAWKS

## NORTHERN RED-SHOULDERED HAWK

*Buteo lineatus lineatus* (Gmelin)
(Lat., *lineatus*, striped)

LOCAL NAME: Chicken Hawk.

RECOGNITION: Adult: Dark reddish brown on back, flecked with whitish; shoulders (bend of wing) chestnut-rufous; white below, barred with reddish brown, heaviest across breast. Tail black, crossed by 4 to 6 narrow white bars.

Immature: Not as red as adult, shows considerable mottling of grays, browns, and rufous; underparts whitish, streaked with dark brown. Tail obscurely barred with brownish. Conspicuous light patches toward end of wings, easily seen in flight.

Length: Male 17 to 23 inches, wingspread 33 to 44 inches; female 19 to 24 inches, spread 39 to 50 inches.

NESTING: Usually in damp woodlands or river bottoms in a variety of tree growth: oaks, pines, cypresses, and mangroves with cabbage palms and cottonwoods, depending on race and range. Elevations vary from 10 to 75 feet. Nest bulky and well made of sticks, twigs, bark strippings, moss, leaves, etc.

Eggs: 2 to 4. White or bluish-white with an endless variety of markings, dots, blotches, and splashes of rich brown, sepia, and purplish drab. Very light at times, when the egg is apt to be nest stained. Measurement 2.35 × 1.75 inches.

RANGE: Breeds from southern Ontario and Quebec, Nova Scotia, and Prince Edward Island south to southern Kansas, northeastern Tennessee, and North Carolina west to the edge of the Great Plains. Winters from southern parts of the northern and central parts of the middle states and southern New England south to the Gulf Coast and Texas.

## FLORIDA RED-SHOULDERED HAWK

*Buteo lineatus alleni* (Ridgway)
(Lat., *alleni*, for J. A. Allen)

RECOGNITION: Somewhat smaller than *B. l. lineatus*, adults much lighter and immatures darker. Head grayish white; underparts pale tan and faintly barred. The general lighter coloration very noticeable.

RANGE: Breeds from Oklahoma, Arkansas, Alabama, and South Carolina south to Louisiana and south central Florida.

## INSULAR RED-SHOULDERED HAWK

*Buteo lineatus extimus* (Bangs)
(Lat., *extimus*, the most remote, referring to extreme southern range)

RECOGNITION: Similar to *B. l. alleni* but even paler, so much so as to suggest albinism. Slightly smaller also.

RANGE: Florida Keys (A.O.U. Checklist). This designation is somewhat misleading since it occurs regularly on mainland Florida, as well as the Keys, at least as far north as Lake Okeechobee. Breeds sparingly, if at all, in the Keys, but commonly in the mangroves of the Cape Sable area and southwest coast, as well as the cypresses and other hammock growth of the Lower Everglades.

## TEXAS RED-SHOULDERED HAWK

*Buteo lineatus texanus* (Bishop)
(Lat., *texanus*, of Texas)

RECOGNITION: More resembling the Red-bellied Hawk than the other Redshoulders, but larger considerably than any of them. Head and neck more red, often spotted with buff on the breast; more richly reddish below than *lineatus*. Immatures are more buffy below and the dark streakings more numerous.

RANGE: From central southern Texas south into Mexico (Tamaulipas).


## RED-BELLIED HAWK

*Buteo lineatus elegans* (Cassin)
(Lat., *elegans*, elegant)

RECOGNITION: Underparts dark, rich reddish almost obscuring barring. Wings crossbarred, as in other races, and as conspicuous. Tail much as in *B. l. lineatus*.

RANGE: Southern British Columbia south to northern Lower California and northwestern Mexico. Resident in the San Joaquin and Sacramento Valleys and lowlands of San Diego area, also from Marin and Shasta Counties along the coastal strip.


HISTORY. The distinction made by many people between this group of Buteos and the Red-tailed Hawks is to call the former Chicken Hawks and the latter Hen Hawks. Such classification leaves much to be desired. Certainly, it would well repay anyone having an associative interest in these predators to go further and ascertain something of the birds' real status.

The adult Red-shoulder well justifies its name if the immature does not. The rusty patch at the bend of the wing and the conspicuously black-and-white-banded tail at once identify it. The rather obscure looking immature is streaked and mottled in browns, grays, and buffs and has little if any reddish on the shoulders. However, an excellent field mark is the presence of the light "windows" or whitish patches near the ends of the wings. When the bird swoops up to a perch in its characteristic fashion, the patches are very noticeable.

Though occurring commonly in woodlands, the Red-shoulder is also a hawk of open country, where it either sits on an exposed perch or swings in circles against the sky. On the Kissimmee Prairie region of Florida, it often uses fence posts or dead stubs as a lookout stand, and along roads where telephone poles occur it frequently alights on the crossarms. It allows close approach at such times and many visitors to the area express surprise at this contrast to its behavior in most other parts of the country. Numerous bird watchers have secured their first really satisfactory looks at hawks at close range in this prairie sector. The Florida Red-shoulder is a definitely lighter bird than its northern relative, and this character is also remarked upon by those seeing it for the first time.

The race in extreme south Florida and the Keys (*extimus*) is even lighter, being so pale as to suggest albinism. This bird, under the name Insular Red-shoulder, is by no means confined to the Keys and probably does not nest there, but is common on the mainland about Cape Sable and the Everglades and up at least as far north as Lake Okeechobee. The Red-bellied form *(elegans)*, on the other hand, is very dark and in its rich coloration is one of the handsomest of the Red-shoulders.

The cry of these hawks is an excellent aid to knowing them, for it can be recognized before the bird is seen. It has been rendered into the words "kee-you" often repeated, and has a wild inflection and timbre. This call is imitated by the Blue Jay with such absolute fidelity that it is impossible to tell whether a jay or the hawk is responsible. It has been stated that there is a difference in the "quality," but I have observed both hawk and jay over many years and am unable to differentiate between their calls.

Long study has been spent on the diet of these birds of prey, and may be briefly summarized: 65 per cent of the total food of the Red-shouldered Hawks consists of rodents and *less than 2 per cent* of poultry. It is probably condemned as Chicken Hawk instead of rat hawk, mouse hawk, or gopher hawk because the 2 per cent poultry take is largely observed, while the 65 per cent rodent total is not seen. If actual figures rather than percentages are used, it is interesting to note that some of the food study results revealed small mammal remains in 287 stomachs, 7 of which also contained poultry and game birds—an illuminating comparison. Frogs and snakes constitute a considerable proportion of the diet in certain areas.

Birds, both wild and domestic, are undoubtedly taken at times by this hawk, but this predation is carried on mainly by immature hawks which find such prey an easy target. Such individuals, if they seem to have developed a persistent taste for poultry, can readily be controlled. The preponderance of rodents taken by the species as a whole is such that commercial loss is very localized and infrequent.

## BROAD-WINGED HAWK

*Buteo platypterus platypterus* (Vieillot)
(Gr., *platypterus*, broad-winged)

LOCAL NAME: Little Chicken Hawk.

RECOGNITION: One of the smallest Buteos, about crow size.
  Adult: Upperparts dark grayish-brown; underparts white, heavily barred with brownish; throat white; wings white beneath with dark tips; tail dark, crossed with two or three white bands of about equal width.
  Immature: Upperparts buff, streaked with dark brown; underparts similar; tail grayish with several obscure blackish bars.
  Length: Male 13.5 to 16.5 inches, wingspread 32 to 38 inches; female 15 to 19 inches, spread 33 to 39 inches.

NESTING: In forest trees at varying heights, sometimes as low as 10 to 12 feet. Of sticks, twigs, bark strippings, etc., often if not invariably decked with sprigs of green leaves.
  Eggs: Usually 2, sometimes 3, rarely 4. Pale bluish-white, variously and endlessly marked with splashes of dark and light browns and drabs; often with small lavender markings. Occasional eggs are immaculate. Measurement 1.90 × 1.55 inches.

RANGE: Breeds from central Prairie Provinces to Ontario, Quebec, and Cape Breton Island south to the Gulf Coast and central Texas, mainly east of the Mississippi River. Winters from south Florida and southern Mexico through Central America to Peru. Reported at times from as far north as southern New England, West Virginia, the middle states, South Carolina, and Georgia.

HISTORY. Several characteristics of this little Buteo set it apart from the others. Together with the localized Short-tailed Hawk and Mexican Goshawk, it is the smallest of the family. It is an unsuspicious bird, showing remarkable tameness. It rarely takes other birds and practically never preys upon poultry. However, it is not immune to ill treatment. Another of its traits is the tendency to travel together in considerable numbers during migration. Following the ridges of the eastern mountains, the hawks fly low at times, and are shot by thoughtless or ignorant gunners. This practice has gone on for years and was a reason for the setting up and maintenance of the present Hawk Mountain Sanctuary. The needless sacrifice of thousands of Broad-wings along the Appalachians is, indeed, a blot on the page of wildlife history.

The small size of the Broad-wing, its typical Buteo contour, and the dark tail with its two or three white bands of almost equal width will identify it to anyone willing to look twice. The close approach it often allows is also diagnostic and is a surprise to many making their first acquaintance with the bird. For a hawk, it is too tame for its own good, resembling in this respect the Everglade Kite. It shares the family character of soaring in wide circles, but varies this by sometimes hovering stationary on beating wings like a Kingfisher or Osprey.

The cry of the Broad-wing is a peculiar sound, a high whistle which has been likened to the note of the Wood Pewee. Rendered into words it might be described as a long "kree-ee-ee-e."

This hawk is definitely insectivorous, though small mammals figure in the diet at times to a considerable extent. Insects taken include quite a variety, but preference is given moth larvae, grasshoppers, and caterpillars. Mammals are represented by mice, rats, red squirrels, chipmunks, rabbits, and shrews. Frogs and snakes occasionally seem to predominate in some localities. Figures resulting from examination by several ornithologists of 254 stomachs of the Broad-wing tell a clear story. Of this number not one contained poultry or game birds; 114 held insect remains and 95 mammal debris. It would appear obvious that the presence of a pair of these hawks around a farm, or anywhere else, would constitute an asset of high value. It is equally obvious that the term Chicken Hawk often applied to the bird is undeserved and erroneous.

## SWAINSON'S HAWK

*Buteo swainsoni* (Bonaparte)
(Lat., *swainsoni*, for William Swainson)

LOCAL NAMES: Prairie Hawk, Gopher Hawk.

RECOGNITION: Possesses two color phases, light and dark, much individual variation between extremes, sometimes rendering identification difficult.

Adult: Male, light phase: upperparts dark grayish-brown; forehead, chin, and throat white; breast broadly banded with chestnut, thinly streaked with black. Remaining underparts creamy or white, with spots and bars of brownish; tail tinged with light gray and crossed by 9 to 12 narrow, indistinct bands.

Female, light phase: Similar to male, but breast band gray-brown rather than chestnut.

Immature: Upperparts dark brown; head, neck, and underparts buffy white, streaked and spotted with drop-shaped markings more numerous on breast. Tail obscurely barred.

Dark phase: Almost entire plumage dark sooty brown, with ash-colored bars on the tail. A wide variety of intergrading occurs between the two phases.

Length: Male 19 to 21 inches, wingspread 47 to 51 inches; female, 19 to 22 inches, spread 47 to 57 inches.

NESTING: Typical Buteo structure of sticks, twigs, and grass, lined with bark strippings and green leaves, lichens, and down. Elevation varies widely; nests have been found from only 7 feet above the ground to as much as 100, average being from 20 to 40. Has been known to nest on the ground.

Eggs: 2 to 4. White or bluish-white, often without markings, but when these appear are irregular and sparing, of various shades of brown, buff, and cinnamon. Measurement 2.20 × 1.70 inches.

RANGE: Breeds from Fort Yukon, Great Slave Lake, and interior British Columbia and Manitoba south to northern Mexico. Winters mainly well below the Equator into southern South America. Casual in the east, reported from eastern Canada, New England, Michigan, New York, South Carolina, and Florida.

HISTORY. Typical of the Great Plains, deserts, and mountains, this aerial westerner seems an entirely appropriate bit of animated scenery. Though a Buteo in fact, and in much of its behavior, Swainson's Hawk often pursues a method of hunting more reminiscent of a Harrier (Marsh Hawk). This consists in flying low over the prairie, quartering back and forth, and making a sudden pounce on ground squirrel or gopher. Now and then it maintains a lookout from a telephone pole or fence post and even descends to the very ground itself. Here it progresses by hopping about briskly or making a sort of half run with raised wings, in pursuit of grasshoppers and crickets. Strange as this behavior may seem for a Buteo, it further varies custom by aerial feeding like the kites.

Recognition of this hawk in the field is sometimes a difficult matter because of the wide individual variation in plumage. All sorts of intergrades take place between the two color phases of the bird, light and dark. Extremes of either are not difficult, but distance and light play queer tricks and are frequently confusing. Typical specimens in the light phase show a gray-brown back, dark gray tail with several darker crossbars, and white underparts, the breast crossed with a wide chestnut band. Forehead, chin, and. throat are white. In the dark phase, extreme examples are an

**COOPER'S HAWK**

Adult perched, immature in flight

**RED-TAILED HAWK**

Adults at left, immatures at right

**RED-SHOULDERED HAWK**

Adults at left and in flight, immature at right

**BROAD-WINGED HAWK**

Adults at left and in flight, immature at right

## SWAINSON'S HAWK

Adult male in light phase on stump, immature on rock,
dark and light phases in flight

**ZONE-TAILED HAWK**
Adults

SENNETT'S WHITE-TAILED HAWK
Adults perched and above, immature in center

**SHORT-TAILED HAWK**

Light and dark phases

almost uniform sooty brown with ashy bars on the tail. Dark color, of course, prevails in others. The hunting behavior is a good field character in contrast to other Buteos.

Though a western species, Swainson's Hawk has wandered widely at times and has been recorded in several eastern localities. Probably the most astonishing illustration of its extralimital occurrence took place in far southern Florida in the late fall of 1952. It suddenly appeared in the Homestead area (25 miles south of Miami) by dozens and scores, frequenting the great truck fields, following tractors and other farm machinery, hopping about amid the furrows, catching insects and rodents. The hawks remained for weeks and created quite a sensation among local bird watchers.

A similar invasion took place the following fall and winter, as many as 150 birds being noted in a day. Nothing like it has ever occurred before and there seems to be no explanation. The ground-feeding procedure was abundantly evident and it is certain that great numbers of insects were destroyed.

In this connection, it is interesting to hark back to some observations of surface feeding in the West years ago. A. K. Fisher (1893) quotes C. Hart Merriam as follows, regarding the latter's experience in Oregon:

We were astonished to see a very large number of large hawks hopping about on the ground, catching grasshoppers. . . . We counted about 150 . . . and there must have been at least 200 in the immediate neighborhood. . . . Two of the three whose stomachs were examined contained grasshoppers and no other food. The third contained, in addition to grasshoppers, the head of a meadow mouse. One contained 88 grasshoppers, another 96, and the third 106 . . . assuming that each hawk captured 200 grasshoppers a day and that there were 200 hawks, the daily catch would be 40,000 grasshoppers. At this rate these hawks would destroy 200,000 grasshoppers in a week and 1,200,000 in a month.

Though no detailed analysis of the food taken by the hawks which appeared in Florida was made, it seems certain that grasshoppers and crickets figured extensively. The resulting benefit to crops from such control is obvious. Examinations made in the West some years ago of 44 stomachs of this hawk showed insects in 31 and mammals in 10. Striped gophers, mice, and ground squirrels make up the bulk of the mammal food. Indeed, every phase of the Swainson's Hawk diet seems to warrant its encouragement and protection as a valuable asset to agriculture.

Swainson's Hawk very rarely attacks poultry or game birds. Indeed, no less an authority than A. C. Bent (1937) says: "I can find no evidence that this hawk ever attacks poultry or gamebirds, and most observers agree that it seldom, if ever, kills birds of any kind." The statement is well borne out by the actions and behavior of small birds which live in close proximity to Swainson's Hawk. They appear completely indifferent to its presence and some species actually build their homes in the sides of this hawk's nest. Again quoting Bent, we find the following in his *Life Histories of North American Birds of Prey*: "English Sparrows and House Finches and also Mourning Doves have been known to build their nests in the lower parts of a Swainson's Hawk's nest." He quotes Frank Stephens as having found Oriole, Kingbird, and House Finch nests in the structure of a Swainson's nest, "all occupied at the same time." Other observers have noted nests of this Buteo in the same tree with those of the Plain Titmouse, Western Bluebird, and Violet-green Swallow. Such evidence leaves no doubt as to the attitude of small passerine birds to the presence of this raptor, as well as the latter's tolerance for them.

## ZONE-TAILED HAWK

*Buteo albonotatus* (Kaup)
(Lat., *albonotatus*, white-marked)

LOCAL NAME: Band-tailed Hawk.

RECOGNITION: Adult: Uniform black except for white forehead and three broad light bands across tail; legs and feet yellow.

Immature: Similar but tail gray-brown, crossed by several narrow diagonal black lines.

Length: 18.5 to 21.5 inches; wingspread 47 to 53 inches.

NESTING: In U.S., usually in cottonwoods at considerable heights, composed of sticks, lined with green cottonwood leaves.

Eggs: 2, sometimes 1, and occasionally 3. Usually pale bluish-white, unmarked; at times with faint spots of lavender and yellowish-brown, concentrated about one end or the other. Measurement 2.15 × 1.70 inches.

RANGE: Extreme southern California eastward through Arizona, New Mexico, and southwest Texas along the Mexican Border south through Lower California and Mexico, Central America, and northern South America in the coast region of Colombia and Venezuela.

HISTORY. This dark raptor occupies so limited a range in this country as to be all but unknown except to those who look for it. Essentially a Mexican and Central American species, it reaches the northern periphery of its range in the Southwest, occurring as far east, at times, as the Rio Grande Valley of Texas. Its economic status is therefore hardly comparable to its many relatives so much more familiar in the United States. Nevertheless, its role of rodent control in the sections it frequents has a definite value, transcended perhaps by its attraction to bird students.

I have never been fortunate enough to see this hawk, though I have looked for it through much of its range. Observers who have studied it in the field have been impressed with its resemblance to the Turkey Vulture. The flight is somewhat sluggish and the wings are often held at an angle over the body, while the bird tilts and veers in a manner similar to the vulture. At other times its behavior is typical of a Buteo in soaring on flatly outspread wings and fanned tail.

Recognition should present little difficulty except for the general resemblance to the Mexican Black Hawk, but the latter carries a very wide white band across the middle of the tail while the present species has three narrower ones, mainly ashy-gray rather than white.

May (1935) observes: "In search of prey these birds often frequent canyons 'where they circle about scouring the cliffs, or, mounting high in the air, dive screaming almost to the water at the bottom,' and at other times their actions are much like those of a Marsh Hawk while hunting. Occasionally, when in pursuit of fish, they hover over the water like an Osprey or a huge Kingfisher. Their cry is said to be very much like that of the Broad-winged Hawk but more piercing and not so highly pitched."

The food of the Zone-tail appears to be largely lizards, frogs, small mammals, and fish, the last item somewhat out of character for most of the Buteos. In securing them it hovers at times, like the Osprey, while sighting and preparing to descend.

## SENNETT'S WHITE-TAILED HAWK

*Buteo albicaudatus hypospodius* (Gurney)
(Lat., *albicaudatus*, white-tailed; Gr., *hypospodius*, lighter gray)

LOCAL NAMES: Prairie Hawk, White-breasted Hawk.

RECOGNITION: Adult male: Upperparts slate or bluish-gray, wing coverts chestnut; underparts pure white lightly marked with fine dusky bars; rump and tail white or lightly barred, tail with a wide blackish subterminal band.

Adult female: Generally darker with the chestnut wing coverts more extensive.

Immature: Upperparts brownish black mottled with reddish; underparts brown marked with yellowish-brown, buff, and white; tail gray-brown, darker toward end and crossed with narrow dusky bars. Some immatures darker than others.

Length: Male and female about 24 inches; wingspread 48 to 54 inches.

NESTING: A large structure of sticks and twigs often placed on top of a yucca, sometimes in a tall bush with no attempt at concealment, being very conspicuous. Elevations vary but are always low, from only a couple of feet to about 15.

Eggs: 2, sometimes 3, rarely 4. Usually pale bluish-white unmarked, but at times sparingly marked with dots of dull brown, buff, or pinkish buff with underlying lavender spots. Measurement 2.25 × 1.80 inches.

RANGE: Lower Rio Grande Valley of Texas south through Mexico and Central America into Colombia and Venezuela.

HISTORY. This fine large hawk occurs in the United States only in south Texas. Formerly it was quite common, but is becoming more and more localized and harder to find. In the late 1930's I saw them regularly on sanctuary inspection trips to the Brownsville area and examined several nests in their typical locations atop yuccas (Spanish bayonets). The reduction of so much of what is called "brush" in the Lower Rio Grande Valley has had its impact on the population of this striking bird, though the large cattle ranches in the area may continue to give it the kind of country it needs. It is a hawk of the wide open spaces of prairie and grasslands, where it may be seen perched atop a bush, fence post, or telephone pole on the lookout for prey. At times it alights on the ground itself, and it is, of course, given to the family trait of wide soaring in the sky. Though not excessively shy, it leaves the nest long before an intruder comes up, since the nests are so placed as to command an extensive view for a long distance around.

The food of the White-tail is largely composed of wood rats and rabbits, remains of both often littering the nest or immediate vicinity. Formerly, rabbits swarmed over the range of this species, but ever advancing civilization has cut heavily into their numbers. Diminution of food supply and alteration of habitat are a combination of factors detrimental, if not disastrous, to any wildlife species, and the White-tail is far less in evidence now than only a few years ago. It seldom seems to molest other birds; indeed some observers who know it well have stated that they never found any evidence of such predation. Others have noted sporadic instances of preying on domestic fowl.

Recognition of this hawk is far less difficult than with others of its range, notably the Western Red-tail and Swainson's. The large size, pure white underparts, and white rump and tail with its black band near the tip will identify it at any reasonable distance and light.

In describing the bird's call, May (1935) says: "When disturbed at its nest its cries are said to resemble the scream of the Red-tailed Hawk and by others are said to suggest the call of a Cooper's Hawk but with a higher pitched, tinkling, musical quality, consisting of the syllables *ke-ke-ke* repeated many times."

There appear to be only two instances of this hawk ever having been recorded outside of Texas, both in Arizona, with a certain element of doubt surrounding them. Even disregarding the White-tail's ecological and economic usefulness, its value as a characteristic and attractive bit of animated life in a region rather barren and wild would amply justify complete protection.

## SHORT-TAILED HAWK

*Buteo brachyurus* (Vieillot)
(Gr., *brachyurus*, short-tailed)

LOCAL NAME: Little Black Hawk.

RECOGNITION: A dichromatic species, the dark phase not representing melanism.

Adult in light phase: Upperparts dark slaty gray, underparts pure white, sides of breast brownish; tail crossed by 7 black and white bands showing grayish below.

Adult in dark phase: Uniform brownish black with white forehead; tail gray crossed with black bands.

Length: About 17 inches; wingspread about 35 inches.

NESTING: In trees of varying species, gum, pine, magnolia, and cypress, from elevations of 15 to 60 feet. The only two nests ever seen by the writer were in a cabbage palm and red mangrove. Made of twigs, lined with moss and green cypress leaves.

Eggs: 2, rarely 3. Pale bluish-white sometimes unmarked; others are

splashed and marbled with various shades of brown. Measurement 2.15×
1.60 inches.

RANGE: Portions of south central Florida and eastern Mexico south through
Central America, Peru, Bolivia, and Brazil.

HISTORY. This is one of the rarer hawks of the country and occurs
only in Florida. Ranging through the northern two thirds of South
America, all of Central America, and part of Mexico, it barely
touches the United States in the only state penetrated by the Tropic
Zone.

One of the smallest of the Buteos, it is about the size of the
Broad-winged Hawk and has two definite color phases, light and
dark. The latter is not melanism, such as is shown by the much
larger Red-tail and Swainson's Hawks, but an example of true
dichromatism.

Bent (1937) paints a rather gloomy picture of its status in
this country, saying: "It always has been extremely rare and
local even there [Florida] and now I believe it has almost, if not
quite, disappeared from that state." No one would be more pleased
than Mr. Bent to be assured that this beautiful little hawk is now
not faring so badly. In recent years it has shown a definite improvement and is readily seen in at least the southern tip of Florida.

True, it has vanished from many former haunts, and in one of
them, the Istokpoga-Okeechobee Lakes region, is now uncommon.
I have seen it only twice there in the past five years, but visitors on
the Audubon Wildlife Tours into the southern Everglades see it
on nearly every trip. It may well be that Audubon warden protection, now followed by the creation of the Everglades National Park,
is responsible for the continued presence of the bird there.

Though of small size its typical Buteo contours help identification at a distance and any reasonably close view will establish it at
once. In the dark phase it appears all black from above, but seen
from below the somewhat lighter wings and tail offer contrast to

the black body. In the light phase it is simply very dark brown above and shining white below, from chin to tail. The tail is crossed with several black and white bands which appear grayish when seen from below.

Generally speaking, it is a rather tame and unsuspicious bird, certainly about the nest.

Aside from any possible encouragement from the general public, or even the enactment of protective laws, the future of the Short-tail in Florida seems assured because of the Everglades National Park. The great majority of its range lies within the limits of the park; its status is that of a resident breeding species. Complete protection is afforded within the park limits and it is not too much to expect that it will, in future, gradually extend its range to re-occupy something of its former area.

Given to the wide soaring so characteristic of its family, this striking little Buteo may be seen at times circling with the Swallow-tailed Kite, high-flying vultures, and Insular Red-shouldered Hawks.

Very little is known of this hawk's food habits. A stomach examined many years ago by A. K. Fisher contained the somewhat incongruous remains of a Sharp-shinned Hawk! The bird takes lizards in the tropics and doubtless does in Florida. I once saw a Short-tail carrying a small snake. Insects are probably consumed as well as reptiles and possibly a few small birds at times, plus mammals.

# ROUGH-LEGGED HAWK

*Buteo lagopus sancti-johannis* (Gmelin)
(Gr., *lagopus*, hare-footed; Lat., *s-johannis*, of St. John's [Newfoundland])

LOCAL NAMES: Rough-legged Buzzard, Mouse Hawk, Squalling Hawk (summer range).

RECOGNITION: A very large Buteo of two color phases (with wide individual variation).

Adult, light phase: Head, neck, and back light buff to white, streaked with brown; base of tail and underwing surfaces white, with black tips to tail and primaries; a definite "wrist-mark" and broad dark brownish or blackish band across abdomen (sometimes lacking). Most constant character is the *basal* white of the tail.

Adult, dark phase: Black or sooty brown, with often a white forehead and much lightness (white) at base of tail. Frequent intergrading between the two extremes.

Immature: The dark band on abdomen usually more solid than in light-phase adults.

Legs feathered to the toes in all plumages.

Length: Male 19 to 22 inches, wingspread 48 to 52 inches; female 21 to 24 inches, wingspread 52 to 56 inches.

NESTING: Sometimes on ledges of cliffs but more often in trees (pines or spruce) near the top. Nest large and bulky, of sticks, twigs, and various debris, lined with grass and feathers.

Eggs: 3 to 5. Bluish-white, boldly splashed with dark brown markings, with much variation. Measurement $2.25 \times 1.75$ inches.

RANGE: Breeds from the Aleutian Islands and Arctic coast of Alaska across to Baffin Island, Ungava, and Labrador south to northern Alberta and the north shore of the Gulf of St. Lawrence and Newfoundland. Winters from southern Canada and northern U.S. south to southern California, New Mexico, Texas, Louisiana, the Carolinas, and Florida. Accidental in Bermuda. (Specimens of a Siberian race of this hawk [*pallidus*, pale *kamtchatkensis*, of Kamchatka] have been taken at St. Michael's, Alaska. It is larger and paler than the North American form.)

HISTORY. This splendid species is the largest of the Buteo hawks, approaching the eagle in size. Far northern in its nesting, it occurs in the United States as a winter bird, but occupies a tremendous range in its seasonal wanderings. Essentially an open-country dweller, it is more often to be seen in prairie or brush regions than in woodlands. Aside from the type of its chosen haunts, the general size and behavior of the Rough-leg provide clues to ready recognition. It varies its hunting tactics between coursing low over prairie or meadow and "still-hunting"—sitting atop some outcropping of rock or low isolated tree, watching for its prey.

When in flight it suggests, by its measured quartering of an area, either a huge Marsh Hawk or an owl. Frequently it indulges the habit of hunting at dusk; indeed, such time of day seems to be a favorite hour. This hawk shares the family trait of soaring at high altitudes at times; its great size is helpful in identifying it, as well as the widespread primaries which are separated like fingers. A characteristic habit is that of hovering motionless in the air on heavily beating wings, exactly like the Kingfisher, Sparrow Hawk, or Osprey. Such behavior may be followed by a plummetlike drop to the ground or a resuming of slow, circling flight.

The bird is described by May (1935) as "the most crepuscular of our hawks. Its flight is usually slow, measured and noiseless, and, with its habit of hunting at dusk, suggests that of some great owl. . . . During direct flight the tail is usually closed, but, when soaring, it is spread open like a fan. Occasionally the bird hovers in one spot, sometimes dropping its legs as though about to pounce upon its prey, and then, apparently changing its mind, drawing them up again under its tail. When wind conditions are just right it sometimes will hold itself stationary in one spot in the air, without hovering, for some moments, in an upcurrent above a hillside. When perched, it sits very erect but low, and its closed wings extend nearly to the end of its tail."

Like others of the Buteo hawks, the Rough-leg has two color phases, light and dark. The former is far easier to recognize because the contrasting light upper breast is in direct comparison to the almost blackish area of the lower parts; the base of the tail is almost white, a good field character; a wide dark band appears at the tip. The dark phase presents problems of identification by reason of similar phases in other hawks of open western country, such as the Red-tailed, Swainson's, and Ferruginous Rough-leg. In the present species a specimen may be all but completely blackish except for the whitish basal tail patch. The legs are feathered to the toes, forming a noticeable "boot" which is responsible for the name "rough-legged."

During its winter wanderings this species may, and sometimes does, penetrate far to the southward. I have seen it four times in coastal South Carolina and several times in south-central Florida. A most remarkable observation was related to me at Okeechobee, Florida, by the then Audubon Warden of that area, Marvin Chandler, as we were watching a specimen of this species near Lake Okeechobee in 1938. Somewhat excited at seeing the bird there myself, I was exclaiming about it when Chandler calmly remarked that he had seen this kind of hawk before and that *it had once nested on the Lake*. This was so remarkable that I questioned him closely on the identification, but he persistently adhered to his story. A day or two later he showed me the nest which had been used. It was on a small island or "reef" as the lake fishermen call it, and was a great pile of sticks and trash on the ground at the highest part of the islet. When Chandler found it, it contained two eggs; he watched it carefully and banded the young when they were hatched. He thought it to be "some kind of eagle" because of its great size, but knew it was not the Bald Eagle, with which he was completely familiar. Many of the fishing guides who worked in that part of the lake knew about the nest, but none of them had seen such a bird before and wondered what it was. These men, though uninformed about ornithology, know the birds of the region well and can at once tell whether a bird is new to them or not. Nothing has subsequently been heard of the banded young. I have recorded this observation in the *Auk*, 57:564, 1940 (the official organ of the American Ornithologists' Union), and *Florida Bird-life*, 1954, p. 114. I have no explanation to offer for such an astonishing occurrence—the nesting of arctic species practically in the tropics, if indeed it was such species. The Rough-leg has been seen in winter by reliable observers in the Okeechobee region on several occasions.

The food preferences of this large raptor have been noted by many ornithologists as being mainly rodents. It is by no means a "bird" hawk; indeed, ptarmigan and ducks, which frequent the same nesting area with it, appear to disregard the presence of the hawk completely. Various small mammal remains have been found in both stomach contents and regurgitated pellets of the Rough-leg. Meadow mice, voles, prairie dogs, lemmings, and gophers figure heavily in the diet. It follows, then, that this hawk is a natural control on these highly reproductive rodents and must be considered as a balance to their sometimes swarming populations. In something over 200 stomachs of this hawk which were examined, 200 contained mammal remains while 10 held birds.

It is one of the most majestic of the birds of prey and an alluring asset to the wide-open spaces of tundra, prairie, and marshland.

## FERRUGINOUS ROUGH-LEGGED HAWK

*Buteo regalis* (Gray)
(Lat., *regalis,* regal)

LOCAL NAMES: Squirrel Hawk, Gopher Hawk, Rusty Hawk.

RECOGNITION: A very large Buteo with two color phases which often intergrade.

Adult, light phase: Upperparts blackish and chestnut, the latter prominent on rump and shoulders; tail pale, reddish-white above, yellowish-white below, varying to almost white, but more so at base, sometimes with an indefinite dark subterminal band; head very light, streaked with dark brownish; underparts practically white except for a few chestnut bars on flanks and belly. Thighs (boots) bright reddish, barred with blackish, contrasting with white belly; undersurface of wings mostly white.

Adult, dark phase: Dark brown to black, with rusty markings frequently with the whitish tail of the light phase, sometimes barred with narrow whitish bands. A light area at base of primaries.

Immature: Brownish gray above; legs and thighs lighter than in adults; tail often with four dark bars.

Length: 22.5 to 25 inches; wingspread about 56 inches.

NESTING: Either in trees or on ledges of cliffs and buttes. Nest of sticks and various grasses or other such vegetation, lined with finer material and feathers.

Eggs: 3 or 4. White, beautifully marked with shades of brown and blackish in endless variation; among the handsomest of the birds of prey. Measurement averages $2.00 \times 2.00$ inches.

RANGE: Breeds from southern and western Canada to northeast California, eastern Oregon and Utah, southern Arizona, New Mexico, and Kansas. Winters from California and Montana to Lower California and northern Mexico. Casual east of the Mississippi River (Wisconsin and Illinois).

HISTORY. Although resembling its relative, the Rough-legged Hawk, in habits and behavior, this species is definitely more southern in distribution, as a glance at the Range will show. It prefers open prairie country and "badlands"—the latter much cut up by erosion into buttes, arroyos, and canyons. Its hunting tactics embrace both flight and watching for prey from the top of some eminence. On the wing, its progress seems rather slow and labored because of the heavy wingbeats, but when soaring at high elevations, as this hawk often does, it is a graceful and accomplished aerialist. Under these conditions it is sometimes mistaken for an eagle.

The rusty (ferruginous) hue of the upperparts, with that of the thighs and legs, is distinctive, together with the almost entirely white underbody. It is well to bear in mind that the dark abdominal band of the Rough-legged Hawk does not appear in this species. The size of the Ferruginous Rough-leg exceeds that of all raptores except the Osprey and the eagles. This size, together with the bird's tameness and habit of perching at low elevations, renders it a seemingly irresistible target for thoughtless gunners. That its destruction is, to say the least, shortsighted is easily proved by the food preferences of this Rough-leg.

The local name of Squirrel Hawk is diagnostic, and it subsists largely on the various ground squirrels (spermophiles) of western country. Other small mammals are included in the diet, such as prairie dogs and wood, kangaroo, and meadow mice. Some snakes and insects are taken by this hawk and, rarely, other birds. P. A. Taverner, one of the outstanding ornithologists of Canada, once found "over a bushel of dried bones and scraps of gophers" around a nest of this species in Alberta. Jack rabbits figure in the food at times. This predilection for mammalian food seems well proven by the fact that 21 of 24 stomachs of the Ferruginous Rough-leg, examined from various parts of its range, contained such food, while two held bird remains.

# HARRIS'S HAWK

*Parabuteo unicinctus harrisi* (Audubon)
(Gr. and Lat., *parabuteo*, near hawk; Lat., *unicinctus*, one-banded; *harrisi*, for Edward Harris)

LOCAL NAME: Black Hawk.

RECOGNITION: Adult: Generally dark brown or blackish; shoulders, under wing coverts and thighs chestnut; primaries black; tail coverts, basal half, and band at tip of tail white; skin between bill and eye, with cere, yellow.

Immature: Head and neck streaked and body feathers with chestnut edgings; underparts buffy with whitish streakings which also appear on upperparts. Tail rather barred.

Length: Male 17.50 to 21 inches; female 21 to 24 inches; wingspread about 45 inches.

NESTING: Varies in elevation from a few feet to 50, of sticks and twigs placed in yucca, mesquite, cactus, and hackberry trees.

Eggs: 3 to 5, white, or pale bluish, usually unmarked but at times show pale spots of lavender, buff, and brown. Measurement 2.10×1.65 inches.

RANGE: Southeastern California eastward through southern Arizona, New Mexico, and Texas, occasionally into Louisiana, south to Panama. (A southern race, *P. U. superior* Van Rossem [Lat., *superior*, larger], occurs in western Mexico and lower California, sometimes reaching southern California and Arizona.)

HISTORY. This large dark-colored hawk occupies only a narrow strip of the southern United States, but is apt to occur farther to the eastward than others of the tropical birds of prey, such as the Zone-tailed, Mexican Goshawk, and Black Hawk. Curiously enough, the "type locality" (where it was first taken) is outside the normal range entirely, for Audubon secured the first specimen in the Bayou Sara area of Louisiana. He named it for his friend Edward Harris. Though said to appear in Louisiana still at times, it is a very rare bird there today, if it occurs at all.

Its present range extends along the Mexican Border from California to Brownsville, Texas, and thence up the coastal plain to about the area from Corpus Christi to Houston. It is, therefore, hardly to be considered important in an economic sense in this country, but its presence is ever a lure to the increasing number of bird watchers. The Southwest has, in this hawk, an asset of definite value.

Harris's Hawk frequents the chaparral type of habitat. It spends much time on the ground, in this respect resembling the Caracara, and often uses no more elevation in perching than low bushes and trees. However, with such rather un-Buteolike tendencies, it combines the characteristic soaring tactics of the family and swings about in wide circles high in the sky.

All the specimens I have seen were observed in the coastal plain of Texas from 1935 to 1940. Most of them were seen perched and rather inactive, allowing close approach before the bird took off. None of them was seen at carrion, though the species is said to consume such at times, again reminding one of the Caracara.

The usual diet consists of small mammals and reptiles, occasionally birds. Rabbits, cotton rats, mice, ground squirrels, lizards, and snakes are taken more or less regularly. W. L. Dawson states that this hawk "has never been known to kill birds, let alone hens" in California.

# MEXICAN GOSHAWK

*Buteo nitida maxima* Van Rossem
(Lat., *nitida*, bright; *maxima*, great)

RECOGNITION: Adult: Upperparts ash-gray barred with darker shades; rump white; tail black, crossed by two or three white bands and white tip. Chin and undertail coverts white; rest of underparts finely barred with gray and white.

Immature: Upperparts sooty brownish, streaked on the head with buff and spotted on wings; rump white; tail gray with 6 to 7 blackish bands and a white tip; underparts broadly streaked with brown; throat sides and underwings buffy.

Length: 16 to 18 inches; wingspread 32 to 38 inches.

NESTING: Of small sticks and twigs lined with green leaves. Usually in mesquite bushes or trees from 25 to 60 feet up.

Eggs: 2 or 3. Usually unmarked pale bluish-white, though often nest-stained. Occasionally, light brown spotting appears. Measurement 1.95 × 1.60 inches.

RANGE: Southern Arizona, New Mexico, and the Lower Rio Grande Valley South to Guatemala. Winters south of the U.S. border.

HISTORY. This species is another of the "borderline" birds of prey of the United States. Occurring along the Mexican line from Arizona to Brownsville, Texas, it is consequently one of the lesser known hawks. It shares, with many other birds, the misfortune of being ill named. It is really no Goshawk at all, though its appearance is strongly similar. Indeed, though more closely related to the Buteos, it might be termed a conglomerate, for it combines characteristics of that family as well as those of the Accipiters and Falcons.

It frequents open country, often in the vicinity of water, which at times exists very locally in its range. The result is that the bird may be irregular within such-confines. Constituting no economic problem, it is much sought after by bird students who visit the

**ROUGH-LEGGED HAWK**

Light and dark phases above

**FERRUGINOUS ROUGH-LEGGED HAWK**

Light and dark phases in background

**HARRIS'S HAWK**

Adults

**MEXICAN GOSHAWK**

Adult at right, immature at left

MEXICAN BLACK HAWK

Adults

**GOLDEN EAGLE**

Adult on ground, immature in flight

AMERICAN or BALD EAGLE

Adult perched, immature in flight

**GRAY SEA EAGLE**

Adult

Southwest, and provides a red-letter experience when seen. Its general status is much like that of such species as the Mexican Black Hawk, Zone-tailed Hawk, and Aplomado Falcon, all of these occupying much the same limited range within this country.

The Mexican Goshawk, says Frank Stephens, "is a rather noisy bird at times. One of its notes is described as a loud *crurr, crurr,* or *cree-u-u,* repeated several times and suggestive of the scream of a distant Peacock."

The food habits of this hawk differ considerably from those of the Goshawk, though, as previously mentioned, there is no real parallel between the birds except for name. The present species takes reptiles, mammals, birds, and insects, the latter often secured on the wing and devoured in the air, a trait reminiscent of the Falcons. Though it takes occasional young game birds at times, the population of the Mexican Goshawk in this country is not sufficient to make it a factor in game bird survival. Besides, it is now well recognized that predation does not normally have an adverse effect on game populations. The important factors are food and cover. A highly proficient bird in flight, the Mexican Goshawk is given to wide soaring at times, which is illustrative of its buteonine character.

## MEXICAN BLACK HAWK

*Buteogallus anthracina* (Lichtenstein)
(Lat., *Buteogallus,* a hawk cock; Gr., *anthracina,* from *anthrax,* coal)

RECOGNITION: Adult: Uniform dark slaty or black; tail crossed by a wide white central band and tipped with same; a small whitish spot at base of primaries when seen from below; cere, legs, and feet yellow.

Immature: Upperparts blackish streaked with rufous, buff, and white; underparts streaked with black and thighs heavily barred with same color. The contrasting crossbarring and lengthwise streaking are noteworthy.

Length: 20 to 23 inches; wingspread about 48 inches.

NESTING: Made of sticks and twigs, lined with grass, leaves, and pine needles, placed in mesquite, cottonwood, sycamore, and willow trees. Some nests are used year after year and assume large proportions.

Eggs: 1 to 3, dull white sometimes spotted with varying shades of brown and lavender, occasionally immaculate. Measurement 2.25 × 1.80 inches.

RANGE: Southern Arizona to Texas in the Lower Rio Grande Valley south through Mexico and Central America to British Guiana and Peru.

HISTORY. In this species, we have again a bird of prey which barely penetrates the United States border. Typical of Mexico, Central America, and northern South America, this hawk crosses into Arizona and Texas, and can therefore be considered largely as an attractive and interesting invader from the tropics. From the standpoint of the bird-watcher-lister-student, Arizona and Texas would do well to encourage the continued existence of the bird and work for its increase. It constitutes an asset possessed by no other area.

Recognition of this hawk presents no problem, other than possible confusion with the Zone-tail. Both species are very dark, not to say black, but the presence of the wide white band across the middle of the tail and a narrow one at the tip will identify the Black Hawk at once.

The aerial ability of the bird is remarkable, even among a family given to striking flight. G. B. Thomas, who is familiar with it in Central America, states that it excels "any of the hawks, kites or falcons except possibly the Swallow-tailed Kite. The flight is really marvelous, excelling in some particulars even the far-famed Frigate or Man-o-war Bird."

It is partial to the vicinity of watercourses and often sits for long periods in a thick-foliaged tree. In some parts of its range (British Honduras) its food consists mainly of large land crabs. Lizards, snakes, crustaceans, insects, and small mammals are taken, but only a very few birds. It constitutes an asset of high aesthetic value.

# v. The Eagles

SUBFAMILY *Buteoninae*

Largest of American birds of prey except the California Condor, the Eagles are heavy-bodied, with beaks large and strongly hooked, talons long, stout, and needle-pointed. The body plumage is dark, but one species, the Bald Eagle, has a completely white head and tail when adult. They are given to soaring at great altitudes in wide circles, and are always distinguishable at any distance by the large size and flatness across wings. The heads are fully feathered. Four species have been recorded from North America, two of which are resident—Golden and Bald Eagles.

## GOLDEN EAGLE

*Aquila chrysaetos canadensis* (Linnaeus)
(Lat., *aquila*, eagle; Gr., *chrysaetos*, golden eagle; Lat., *canadensis*, of Canada)

LOCAL NAMES: Mountain Eagle, Gray Eagle, Ring-tailed Eagle, War Eagle, Royal Eagle.

RECOGNITION: Adult: Entirely dark brownish (black at a distance) except crown and back of head, which are golden brown; tail and primaries blackish, with light areas at base of primaries, noticeable in flight; *legs feathered to toes.* Beak bluish, cere yellow as are the feet.

Immature: Dark brown except for light areas on chin, lower throat, or upper breast and legs. Scattered light feathers here and there over body; tail with dark terminal band but basal two-thirds whitish (giving rise to local name of Ring-tailed Eagle). This whitish area diminishes with age.

Length: Male 30 to 35 inches, wingspread 75 to 84 inches; female 35 to 41 inches, wingspread 82 to 92 inches.

NESTING: A mass of sticks, sometimes very large, lined with grass, leaves, or feathers and moss, measuring as much as 6 to 8 feet across with interior rather shallow. Placed usually on ledges or in niches of cliffs, often at a considerable height from the ground, and well below the upper rim of buttes, mesas, etc. Occasionally trees are utilized, particularly in the Pacific coastal area.

Eggs: 1 to 4. Sometimes very handsomely marked with shades of brown, gray, and lilac on a whitish ground. Some are almost immaculate, or very sparingly spotted. Measurement 2.90 × 2.50 in.

RANGE: Breeds in mountain areas from northern Alaska and Mackenzie south to Lower California, central Mexico, west Texas, and Oklahoma (formerly to North Carolina and may still do so rarely). Winters south to the Gulf Coast (uncommonly) and appears sporadically from northeastern United States down the Blue Ridge Mountains to the southern Atlantic seaboard into Florida.

HISTORY. This splendid species might well be termed the king of birds. Unlike the Bald Eagle, it occurs in Europe as well as this continent and was probably the bird chosen by ancient kingdoms as their emblem. In this country it is essentially western in distribution, more apt to be seen west than east of the Mississippi River. However, a few are noted every year along such migratory routes as Hawk Mountain, in Pennsylvania, visited by so many bird watchers annually, and it is recorded from time to time on the Atlantic seaboard as far south as Florida.

The Golden Eagle derives its name from the light ochraceous-buff feathers of the head and neck. It is a very dark bird otherwise, with a light area about the basal portion of the tail and under the wings. It appears to prefer mountainous regions throughout most of its range and uses cliffs, promontories, and crags for both nesting sites and vantage points from which to watch for prey. Much of its hunting is done while in flight. In its western (normal) range it was highly regarded by the Plains Indians, who used its feathers in their headdresses and for tribal ceremonies.

The Golden Eagle is a bird of considerable size. Its weight runs from about 8 pounds in a small specimen to nearly 13. The wing-spread is about 6.5 feet. Eagles have been generally credited with ability to carry about their own weight. It is the take-off, however, that presents difficulty unless made from an elevation, such as a cliff. Rising from ground level much reduces carrying capacity. Experiments by C. C. Sperry have shown that an 11-pound eagle was unable to rise from the ground with a 5.25-pound weight. Indeed, even with a ground squirrel in its talons, an eagle has been known to take a roundabout route to its nest to utilize advantageous air currents.

This inability to carry much weight proves how ridiculous are the persistent stories of eagles carrying off children. At times the birds do kill prey which they cannot possibly carry, but any attack on man is very rare, though a few are on record. Such instances have resulted from disturbance while feeding or from investigation of the nest.

Eagles are long-lived birds. Twenty-five to thirty years and very possibly more constitute the life span. Though remaining mated for years, eagles will soon remate on the death of one or the other of a pair. Nesting territory varies according to conditions, but J. B. Dixon found, after close study, that the average territory defended by a pair of Golden Eagles in southern California is about 36 square miles.

Any controversy centering on this fine species revolves about its economic status and effect of food habits in relation to man's interests. Though reams of literature have appeared on the matter, much of it is summarized in the most recent and authoritative study made of this species, *The Golden Eagle and Its Economic Status* by Lee W. Arnold, Circular 27, U.S. Fish and Wildlife Service, Washington, D.C.

It is stated by Arnold that this eagle has been known to kill more than sixty forms of animal life, ranging from insects to full-grown deer. Living prey and carrion are eaten. Rodents form the staple diet, varying with local conditions. As a result of this dietary range, the Golden Eagle has been treated with such extremes as complete protection in some localities, because of its control of jack rabbits, to determined elimination in others, because of real or supposed depredations on domestic stock. Illustrative of the latter have been the activities of the Big Bend Eagle Club of west Texas. This is a group of about one hundred ranchers who hire an airplane pilot to hunt eagles in their own element with a light plane. In six years, a total of over 4,800 Golden Eagles have been killed.

Dr. Olaus Murie, president of the Wilderness Society, has presented an interesting slant on the attitude of westerners toward the Golden Eagle in this quotation from an article, "A Price on His Golden Head," that appeared in the July-August, 1952, issue of *Audubon Magazine*:

It is true, of course, that economics and personal welfare are necessary to normal living. It is easy to belittle an economic loss when it is not our own. If we respect our conscience we must be fair. But we have here a social complex that requires fairness on all sides. We need the routine materials for physical existence, but we need as well the resource for spiritual well-being and what we know as happiness. Fortunately, there has been nurtured in the human heart, although at times precariously, what we call generosity. I am happy to say that I have found this among many of those who raise livestock; who deprecate their losses caused by wild creatures by the comment: "Oh, well, I kind of like to see them around."

I resent the organized efforts to assemble statistics to prove to such well-intentioned countrymen that their losses are severe and should be remedied. In other words, I resent propaganda to convince such people that their good natured generosity is misplaced—propaganda to convince them that they are really unhappy, after all.

## BALD EAGLES

### SOUTHERN BALD EAGLE

*Haliaetos leucocephalus leucocephalus* (Linnaeus)
(Gr., *haliaetos*, a sea eagle; *leucocephalus*, white-headed)

LOCAL NAMES: American Eagle, White-headed Eagle, Black Eagle, Gray Eagle (referring to immature), Sea Eagle.

RECOGNITION: Adult: Head, neck, and tail white, rest of plumage dark brownish black; bill, cere, and bare portion of legs. with feet, yellow.

Immature: Uniform grayish or brownish black, mottled with whitish, often much so and increasing with age. Appears all dark at a distance and noticeably larger than adult. Latter plumage attained about 4th year.

Length: Male 30 to 34 inches, wingspread 72 to 85 inches; female 35 to 37 inches, wingspread 79 to 90 inches.

NESTING: Either on cliffs in mountainous areas or in trees elsewhere. A mass of sticks, straw, grass, and moss which, after years of use and additional material, assumes large proportions. Some nests are as much as 9 feet across the top and 15 to 20 feet outside depth. Elevations from the ground differ from the earth itself (cliffs) and as low as 10 feet in mangroves of the Florida Keys to 150 feet in pines and cypresses. Usually placed in a living tree, but on the coast, constant drip of salt water from the plumage sometimes kills the tree. Some nests have been occupied for more than 20 years.

Eggs: 2, rarely 3. White. Measurement 2.75 × 2.10 inches.

RANGE: Whole of U.S. to southern Lower California and central Mexico, breeding throughout in suitable localities. Local in California and some of the interior desert states. Casual in Bermuda.


## NORTHERN BALD EAGLE

*Haliaetos leucocephalus washingtoniensis* (Audubon)
(Lat., *washingtoniensis*, for George Washington)

RECOGNITION: Larger than the Southern Bald Eagle but indistinguishable in the field. Length 34 to 43 inches; wingspread 82 to 98 inches.

RANGE: Breeds in boreal zones from northwestern Alaska, Mackenzie, and Quebec south to British Columbia and the Great Lakes. Winters south to Washington, Montana, and southern New England.


HISTORY. The Bald Eagle should interest everyone by reason of the fact that it is our national emblem. It is a regal bird though some of its behavior hardly measures up to its royal appearance. To see it, swinging in great circles against the sky, the snowy head and tail shining vividly as the sun catches them, is one of the most inspiring sights in nature.

The bird has been aptly described by May (1935) as "an inspiration to all observers and of great esthetic interest, as it soars easily high overhead on wide-spread pinions, or perches, apparently in deep thought, on the jagged summit of some great dead tree beside the shore of a wooded lake or an inlet of the sea."

Despite the selection of this eagle as our national bird by Congress in 1782, it was not until 1940 that it was accorded protection throughout the country, a period of over 150 years. Protection was not extended to Alaskan Bald Eagles until 1952. And even now one sees occasionally in the public press "news" pictures of someone holding up an eagle he has killed, seeming to consider such action a deed of valor and not realizing that he is convicting himself of lawbreaking.

The adult Bald Eagle is hardly to be mistaken for any other bird. However, the uniformly dark, mottled immature can be confused with the Golden Eagle. The bare (unfeathered) leg of the Bald Eagle is a distinctive field character contrasted to that of the Golden Eagle, which is feathered to the toes. The immature Bald Eagle is sometimes confusing to observers, hence one hears such names as Gray, Brown, and Black Eagle, all of which simply indicate the immature Bald Eagle before it attains its adult plumage.

Vultures are sometimes mistaken for eagles, but the distinction between the two is really very simple and can be noted from almost as far as either can be seen in the sky. When soaring, the eagle carries its wings perfectly flat across, while the vultures have a distinct dihedral (V) angle. When perched, the eagles show a large head; vultures' heads are small and insignificant looking. The term "bald-*headed* eagle" is utterly erroneous. In the case of the eagle (as well as with the Baldpate Duck) the world "bald" means *white* and not *bare*.

The Bald Eagle is less aggressive and predatory than the Golden. Any attack on man is extremely rare, and the usual behavior, when the nest is being investigated, is to fly around at a safe distance, yelping thinly, or else to disappear completely until the investigation is over.

Charles Broley, of Guelph, Ontario, and Tampa, Florida, has banded more than 1,300 Bald Eagles since his retirement from banking, and the main danger he reports (aside from climbing 100-foot cypresses and pines) is avoiding the grasp of the talons of the youngsters he handles. He has suffered injuries from the young birds but not from the adults. One of the chief results of his important work is the definite proof that Florida eagles go north in summer as far as the Maritime Provinces of Canada.

Though capable of catching its own fish, the Bald Eagle sometimes relieves the Osprey of its catch; such a performance is a spectacular bit of natural predation to watch. This eagle has been reduced over its former extensive range, but it is still to be seen regularly in the south Atlantic region and Gulf Coast. The northern race, also much reduced by bounties and supposed competition with salmon fisheries, is still found in the northwestern parts of this continent.

Large as they are, eagles can attain considerable speed when the necessity arises—certainly enough to capture some of the ducks. Though the wingbeats seem somewhat labored, there is no doubt about the power they impart and an eagle in a hurry is a sight to remember. The Bald Eagle has a diversified diet. In much of its range it feeds largely on fish; indeed, in the southeastern U.S. such food predominates. About coastal areas the catfish bulks largely in the diet. Some wildfowl are taken, mainly crippled ducks, and often the American Coot. Occasionally mammals, principally rodents, are secured, and at rare intervals poultry and wild birds. I once saw a Bald Eagle in Florida bring a female Mallard to its nest, where it was deposited, then flopped out, fell to the ground, and was picked up by me. There were large wounds in the breast and lower back of the still-alive duck, no doubt inflicted by the eagle's talons. This is the only instance I have ever witnessed of the taking of a game bird other than Coot.

The Bald Eagle feeds on carrion as well as living prey; when, at such times, vultures are also present, the latter stand aside until the eagle is surfeited.

The "scream" of the eagle is apt to be rather disappointing at a first hearing. Most of the bird's vocal attainments consist of a high, thin, but carrying note, a creaky sort of yelp like the sound of a rusty hinge or a small puppy. It can be heard at a considerable distance and sometimes attracts attention even before the bird itself is seen in the sky.

Now and then, eagles can be seen crossing over cities of some size. In former years there were nests of this splendid bird within ten miles of Charleston, South Carolina. In severe winter weather, this eagle is at times seen near New York City, sitting on blocks of ice floating down the Hudson River.


## GRAY SEA EAGLE

*Haliaetus albicilla* (Linnaeus)
(Lat., *albicilla*, white-tailed)

This eagle is an Old World species, resident in Greenland. No more than an accidental wanderer to North America, it has been recorded from the New England coast (Maine and Massachusetts). No economic significance attaches to it and its appearance can never be expected. It is mentioned here because of the past few occasions of its presence and remote possibility of future ones.

The field characters (recognition marks) are the gray head, dark body, and white tail of the adult; immatures show a definitely streaked breast. It is, of course, a very large bird.

# STELLER'S SEA EAGLE

*Thallasoaetus pelagicus* (Pallus)
(Gr., *thallasoaetus*, a sea lifter, referring to its fish-catching ability;
Lat., *pelagicus*, of the sea)

An eagle of Siberia, this species wanders at times to the Aleutian Islands and has twice been recorded from there (Pribilof and Kodiak Islands). It cannot be expected on this continent, certainly not in this country. Its status is somewhat similar to that of the Gray Sea Eagle at the opposite extreme of North America, though the latter has appeared in the United States and this species has not.

The field characters are the wedge-shaped white tail, dark body plumage, with the wing coverts, rump, and thighs being white, as well as the tail.

# VI. The Harriers

SUBFAMILY *Circinae*

The sole representative of this group in North America is the Marsh Hawk. Closely related to the Harriers of the Old World, it is considered by some authorities to be subspecific. The American bird is characterized by long, narrow wings, veering flight, and white patch on the rump.

## MARSH HAWK

*Circus cyaneus hudsonius* (Linnaeus)
(Gr., *circus*, a kind of hawk, *cyaneus*, blue; Lat., *hudsonius,* of Hudson Bay)

LOCAL NAMES: Harrier, Rabbit Hawk, Bullet Hawk, Mouse Hawk.

RECOGNITION: Sexes differ in plumage but both are always easily identified by the white rump patch. Ruff of feathers about the face suggests the Owls.

Male: Pale bluish-gray above; white below with tips of wings black; tail gray with dark bands.

Female: Brown above, darkest at shoulders; light brownish below with longitudinal streaks; tail barred with black and buff.

Immature: Similar to female but darker about the face and underparts less streaked.

Length: Male 17.5 to 20 inches; female 19 to 24 inches; wingspread 43 to 54 inches.

NESTING: On the ground in marsh or prairie areas, usually near water. Nest constructed of grass, sticks, and feathers, the last as a lining. Use of the same site in successive years results in a considerable platform.

Eggs: 4 to 6, usually pale bluish-white but occasionally with a few brownish spots. Both sexes work at nest construction, incubation, and care of the young. Nesting territory is vigorously defended against all comers. Measurement 1.80 × 1.40 inches.

RANGE: Breeds from northwestern Alaska and Mackenzie, northern Manitoba, and Ontario, central Quebec, and Newfoundland south to northern Lower California, southern Arizona, southern Texas, Illinois, Indiana, Ohio, Maryland, and southeastern Virginia. Winters from southern British Columbia, western Montana and South Dakota, southern Wisconsin, Michigan, New York, Vermont, and New Hampshire south to the Bahamas, Florida, Cuba, and Colombia. Accidental in Barbados and Hawaii.

HISTORY. The Marsh Hawk is so essentially a bird of open country that one thinks of it over fields, prairies, and marshes as automatically as a duck is connected with water. Although the range of this hawk is tremendous and many people know it under one or another of its local names, much misunderstanding exists regarding its relation to other wildlife. Such misunderstanding inevitably produces mistaken ideas about the Marsh Hawk's impact upon man's interests. None the less, it is difficult to see how anyone can fail to thrill at the sight of this hawk as a part of the natural scene any more than one would fail to respond to a blazing sunset, or the rosy dawn upon a snow-capped mountain range.

The adult male Marsh Hawk is a handsome bird. There is something reminiscent of a gull about it, not only in its mastery of flight, but its pure white underparts, black-tipped wings, and light-gray mantle. To see one coursing low over the grasstops of a meadow, field, or pasture, veering, tilting, rising and falling with the air currents, pausing to hover momentarily, then either to drop straight down amid the grasses or continue the aerial patrol of the grasslands, is to watch something which remains in one's memory as the image of an efficient, graceful hunter.

The courtship evolutions are thus described by Norman Criddle (1912) as quoted by May: "He usually starts with a sort of wobbly flight as if imitating a tipsy individual, then swooping downwards, he turns completely over, occasionally several times in succession, and then darts up again, with a cackle, to repeat the same performance over again, often tumbling within a few feet of the female which is usually flying below. Occasionally these performances are terminated with the wobbly flight over again, at other times they neither start nor end in this manner. I have also observed the female try her skill in the same way but she lacks the confidence and grace of her husband."

So completely does the Marsh Hawk fit into the air that it is difficult to consider it perched. Indeed, when perched, it confuses observers, for its contours when at rest seem utterly different from the grace of aerial locomotion. When on the wing it well deserves the somewhat overworked designation "unmistakable," for the well-defined white rump patch will always distinguish it. One cannot watch the bird for many seconds without this highly distinctive field character becoming apparent. Such "field mark" is equally applicable in the two sexes and in any stage of plumage. The rather slender body and long tail serve to confirm the identification. During the periods of sailing on motionless wings, there is a distinct dihedral apparent, amounting to as much as 120°.

And what is this accomplished aerialist searching for in so methodically quartering marsh, prairie, and pasture? For that essential on which everything in nature depends—food. And what makes up the Marsh Hawk's food? Here indeed is where conflict of opinion arises; where misunderstanding intrudes and conclusions clash. A glance at some is illustrative.

From Montana (E. S. Cameron) comes the opinion that the Marsh Hawk is one of the most "pertinacious of any" in its depredations upon poultry. From Nevada comes the conclusion (Ridgway) that this hawk takes great numbers of lizards, many stomachs containing nothing else, being literally stuffed. In New Jersey, Urner found that mice, insects, and small birds formed the bulk of the diet. Stoddard in Georgia found the cotton rat to predominate in this hawk's food; from a collection of 1,100 pellets of undigested material taken from a roosting place of Marsh Hawks, 925 held remains of this rodent, 84 per cent of the total food. In British Columbia, Brooks considered this hawk a definite menace to nesting waterfowl, whereas Munro in Alberta found it feeding almost exclusively on rodents.

I have found this hawk preying extensively on the Clapper Rails of the South Carolina coastal marshes, as well as upon cotton rats and other small mammals, such as the marsh rabbit. What does all this mean? Simply that from one corner of the continent to the other, and at varying seasons, the Marsh Hawk eats different food at different times. As a result, observers in British Columbia and Georgia arrive at varying conclusions, both no doubt correct but neither essentially indicative. It is another proof of the danger of belief in "backyard" conclusions. In a continental sense the country is the better off for birds like the Marsh Hawk, not only for economic but also aesthetic reasons.

Regarding its economic role, consider the fact that the rice plantations of Carolina supplied all of that grain to the country prior to the 1860's. Great loss was incurred by planters from depredations on this crop by Bobolinks, or, as they were locally known, Ricebirds. There were years when this loss amounted to as much as $2 million (a million meaning more in those days than it does now). The Marsh Hawk was a positive factor in reducing loss by its habit of hunting—quartering the extensive fields and flushing flocks of Bobolinks (and Blackbirds) which were feeding on the rice. It has been estimated that this was worth as much as $300 in hire of Negroes to do the same thing by beating tin pans, firing guns, and producing other sound effects. Though Carolina does not now figure largely in the rice production of this country, such states as Texas and California do; depredations still occur in such fields, and Marsh Hawks still exist and still pursue their time-honored hunting tactics.

Any southern winter landscape, whether of pasture, marsh, or field, or any northern slough or western meadow without this graceful, low-flying hunter would be lacking a part of what the world of nature needs to render it a balanced unit.

# VII. The Ospreys

FAMILY *Pandioninae*

These birds are specialized fish-eating hawks of a single species and several races, widely distributed over the world. Structurally, the wings and legs are long, the feet large and covered with roughened protuberances which enable them to grasp slippery prey. The outer toes are reversible so that the talons can become paired.

## OSPREY

*Pandion haliaetus carolinensis* (Gmelin)
(Gr., *Pandion*, King of Athens; *haliaetus*, a sea eagle; Lat., *carolinensis*, of Carolina)

LOCAL NAMES: Fish Eagle; Fish Hawk.

RECOGNITION: Adult: Upperparts dark brown; crown streaked with blackish; a black stripe through the eye and down sides of neck, and white line over eye; head, neck, and underparts white; breast somewhat streaked with brownish, accentuated in female. Flight feathers barred on undersurface with tips black with a conspicuous spot on wrist (bend of wing); tail crossed with several bars and narrow white tip. Cere, legs, and feet bluish.

Immature: Pattern similar but back feathers with whitish edges; underparts buffy and tail more numerously barred.

Length: 21 to 24.5 inches; wingspread 54 to 72 inches.

NESTING: A huge mass of sticks, twigs, and moss placed either on the ground, telephone poles, dead stubs, cliffs, or trees. Nest added to year after year and often used for many seasons. If built in living tree, latter often dies from salt water being shaken upon it from the bird's plumage, or from oily and saline deposits from droppings.

**STELLER'S SEA EAGLE**

Adult

**MARSH HAWK**

Adult male flying at left, adult female flying at right, immature perched

**OSPREY**

Adults

**AUDUBON'S CARACARA**

Adults in foreground and flying, immature in background

**WHITE GYRFALCON**

Adult on ground, immature in flight

**BLACK GYRFALCON**

Adult perched, immature in flight

**PRAIRIE FALCON**

Adult male

**DUCK HAWK**

Adult on ground, immature in flight

Eggs: Usually 3, rarely 4. Wide variation in color and markings, among the handsomest of all birds of prey. Ground color of pinkish white often totally obscured by heavy splashes and blotches of rich browns and drabs. Some eggs are heavily wreathed about the large end; rarely they are immaculate. They possess a pungent odor which clings to them for years. Measurement 2.40 × 1.80 inches.

RANGE: Breeds from northwest Alaska across to Hudson Bay, Labrador, and Newfoundland south to Lower California, western Mexico, the Gulf Coast, and Florida Keys. Winters from Florida and the Gulf States through Lower California and Mexico to Central America and the West Indies. Accidental in South America and Greenland, occasional in Bermuda.

HISTORY. This striking hawk should be known to more observers throughout the country than any other, with the possible exception of the Sparrow Hawk, because of its tremendous range. It covers the United States completely and penetrates northward into Arctic Canada and south into western Mexico—a vast area indeed.

As might be readily supposed, the Fish Hawk is not to be found far from sizable bodies of water: lakes, rivers, reservoirs, seacoasts, and the like. Often mistaken for an eagle, it is not as large as that bird and may always be distinguished therefrom by its pure white underparts. When soaring, the wings present a "break" or bend in the middle (wrist joint) which is characteristic and somewhat reminiscent of the Frigate Bird.

The fishing technique is a spectacular performance. When it sights possible prey, the bird hovers momentarily or longer, on heavily beating wings, quite fixed in the air, then plunges downward like a great feathered spearhead. The fish is seized with the talons and the bird at times all but submerges with the force of impact. Rising, it shakes water from the plumage much as a retriever does when coming ashore, shifts the prey so that it heads into the wind, and beats its way to nest or feeding perch. Elevations from which the dive is begun vary from about 25 feet to as much as 100.

The Osprey is an inoffensive bird as a rule, but vigorously

defends its nest against all invaders—even human intruders at times. Though frequently victimized by the eagle and forced to give up its prey, the tables are occasionally turned and the hawk becomes the attacker and, it may be added, the victor.

It is a rare circumstance indeed when the Osprey takes birds of any kind. Small species such as Grackles sometimes build their homes in the sides of an Osprey nest and even Night Herons have been known to do so. Its economic status, though generally favorable, occasionally suffers reversal by reason of its tendency to take fish at hatcheries. Many of the birds have been, and still are, killed for such behavior. Competent control under proved conditions of offense is at times necessary.

Numerous authorities have stated that the Osprey eats nothing but fish. Though this view is doubtless the result of their own observations, there are variations of this diet on record. Undoubtedly, in the vast majority of the birds' range, fish is the exclusive food. The fish taken are of many species, but few of them are of importance to man as food, so few that the Osprey cannot be considered in a competitive sense. In certain western lakes and streams trout are taken and salmon also. Weakfish (squeteague or "winter trout"), mullet, and some shad are human "food" fish of salt water which the bird takes occasionally. However, catfish (salt water) is a staple for the Osprey in the Southeast and Gulf Coasts. Tomcod, carp, perch, sunfish, and suckers are secured also, none of economic importance except the perch. Menhaden and blowfish figure as well. There are persistent reports of the Osprey tackling fish too big for it and being dragged under and drowned. Indeed, there are definite instances of dead birds, attached to a large fish, found on beaches. Such cases, however, are rare and it cannot be supposed that such an efficient species would make the mistake often.

Other items of food on record are frogs, snakes, ducks, *very rarely* chickens, crows, and night herons. Any variation from a piscatorial diet is out of the ordinary and can fairly be considered an abnormality. In forty years of field observation I have seen the Osprey devouring a bird but once. This was at Lake Okeechobee, Florida, in March of 1955. The bird was a blackbird but the hawk was not seen to actually secure it.

The Osprey is encouraged about many fishing communities and aids to its nesting are provided in the shape of wagon wheels on posts, etc., for the fishermen consider that the bird helps in locating schools of fish which would otherwise be missed. Picturesque and attractive, the bird has high aesthetic value and practically every phase of its activity deserves encouragement by complete protection.

# VIII. The Caracaras

SUBFAMILY *Polyborinae*

Caracaras are tropical birds of prey related to the Falcons, but in habit and behavior more resembling the Vultures. Stout-bodied and long-legged, they are markedly terrestrial and walk well. The food is a combination of living prey and carrion.

## AUDUBON'S CARACARA

*Polyborus cheriway auduboni* (Cassin)
(Gr., *polyborus*, very voracious; So. Am., *cheriway*, a name; Lat., *auduboni*, for John J. Audubon)

LOCAL NAMES: Mexican Buzzard, Mexican Eagle.

RECOGNITION: Adult: Skin of face bare and bright orange-red; crown flattened, black, and slightly crested; back, wings, and abdomen black; lower breast white or creamy with fine blackish bars; large white patches in wings and at base of tail, latter white with many narrow blackish bars and wide black terminal band. Feet and legs yellow; bill large and eaglelike.

Immature: Pattern similar but plumage much duller, generally rusty brown instead of black and dingy gray rather than white.

Length: 20 to 25 inches; wingspread about 48 inches.

NESTING: Nest composed of sticks and twigs, lined with moss or leaves. In Florida, placed almost invariably in the tops of cabbage palms (Sabal palmetto), very rarely in live oaks. In the Southwest, in mesquite, oak, elm, and the saguaro cactus.

Eggs: 2 or 3, rarely 4. Creamy white, usually almost obscured by splashes of various shades of brown. Some are spotted with smaller markings and rarely an immaculate one is found. Generally they are quite handsome. Measurement 2.50 × 1.80 inches.

RANGE: Northern Lower California, southwestern Arizona and Texas, parts of south central Florida south through Mexico and Central America.

HISTORY. This striking species is unique among the birds of prey and one of the most interesting. It is the "national bird" of Mexico and appears on the State Seal of that country, hence its local names as given above, though of course it is neither eagle nor buzzard. Discovered in 1831 near St. Augustine, Florida, by John James Audubon, it was named for him.

A definitely terrestrial bird, it is also a proficient flier; taking carrion freely, it also catches considerable living prey; occupying a very limited range in this country, it is readily found where it does occur and often allows close approach. The Caracara is a sort of hawk-eagle-vulture combination of characteristics.

Portions of Arizona, Texas, and Florida comprise its United States range, but because of certain topographical limitations it is more easily observed in Florida. It is a bird of open country; the mesquite brush of Texas, the cactus desert of Arizona, and the palm-hammock-dotted Kissimmee Prairie of Florida make up its chosen homes, where it is resident the entire year. The Caracara derives its name from a Brazilian word which purports to be the sound of its harsh, cackling cry. In Cuba it is known as Caraira. In giving the cry the head is thrown far backward, so much so that the crown almost touches the shoulders, a remarkable contortion. But in the many times I have seen the contortion and heard the cry, it never sounded like "caracara."

It walks with a stately stride, firm and straight, with none of the hopping clumsiness of the vultures with which it is often seen. The adult is a handsome bird in black and white, with the large eagle-like beak and brightly colored face strikingly conspicuous. The flight is strong and usually direct, alternating between flapping and sailing. It can, however, indulge in complicated evolutions when in mating flight or pursuit of prey—twisting, banking, and diving with great speed.

The live prey of the Caracara embraces snakes, turtles and their eggs, small alligators, mammals, insects, and rarely birds of a few species. It is adept at digging out turtle nests and I have seen the bird watch a laying turtle complete its function, then proceed to eat the eggs. The large strong feet are well adapted to digging. In the Southwest, rabbits, prairie dogs, and rats are taken by this bird, and in coastal Texas the Caracara has been known to relieve Pelicans of fish.

Now and then attacks are made on very young pigs and calves, and the action brings condemnation upon this bird. Florida ranchers have it shot in some areas on such grounds, but whether the Caracara is actually responsible for the attacks is a moot question. If so, it is certainly unusual. I have seen a great deal of this bird in Florida for nineteen years and have never witnessed a single instance of its attacking domestic stock. While this experience is not conclusive, it is highly indicative. Its predilection for turtles' eggs is favorable to sport fishing, for turtles are a control on such game fish as the large-mouthed black bass.

The aesthetic value of the bird to the many bird students who visit its range is high, for it is an attractive natural asset.


## GUADALUPE CARACARA

*Polyborus lutosus* Ridgway
(Lat., *lutosus*, muddy, referring to the brown color)

HISTORY. Although it is now extinct, it seems well to include some mention of this species here if for no other reason than a warning. What happened to it could happen to others.

Discovered by Dr. Edward Palmer in 1875 when he visited Guadalupe Island, it was an abundant bird there, known to the natives as Quelelis. By the end of the year 1900 it was extinct. The birds were in the habit of preying on the kids and goats of the islanders, and with the advent of white men and rifles the species only lasted for a few years. Bent (1938) has this to say regarding it: ". . . whenever a beast or bird interferes too much with human interests its days are numbered, unless it proves more than a match for its human enemies, as does the crow. This bird [Caracara] was not endowed with sufficient sagacity to survive. . . ."

Much has been learned in recent years about reducing economic loss from predators; it will greatly mitigate the loss and still preserve the species from extinction. The knowledge came too late for this insular bird, but its destruction will stand as a warning of how easy it is to take away life and the impossibility of restoring it.

The Guadalupe Caracara was a paler and much more brownish bird than Audubon's and with more barring of the plumage. Some 37 specimens are known to be preserved in collections.

# IX. The Falcons

## SUBFAMILY *Falconinae*

These are birds of commanding presence and spectacular hunting tactics, "stooping" (diving) upon prey in full flight. The wings are long, narrow and pointed, tails rather long, and flight fast. The Falcons are inhabitants of open country though two species, Duck Hawk and Sparrow Hawk, occur at times in towns and cities. In the heyday of falconry, these birds were trained to fly from the wrist upon avian prey, which predominates in their diet.

## GYRFALCONS

### WHITE GYRFALCON

> *Falco rusticolus candicans* (Gmelin)
> (Lat., *falco,* a falcon; *rusticolus,* a country dweller; *candicans,* light)

LOCAL NAMES: White Hawk, White Falcon.

RECOGNITION: *Applicable to all races.* Varying from nearly pure white or very light, spotted with dark brown or black, to very dark, almost black. In either extreme there is little contrast between upper and lower parts, but in the case of *F. r. obsoletus* there is sharp definition between dark upperparts and light underparts, which are barred or spotted in the adult and streaked in the immature.
Length: 20 to 25 inches; wingspread 44 to 52 inches.

NESTING: *Applicable to all races.* Usually on cliffs or ledges, often in inaccessible locations, sometimes in old nests of the American Rough-legged Hawk.
Eggs: 3 or 4. Ground color buffy or cream, speckled and blotched with

reddish brown, at times so heavily as all but to obscure the ground color. Eggs of the various races are indistinguishable from each other. Measurements 2.30 × 1.80 inches.

RANGE: Resident in eastern Arctic America and Greenland. Casual in winter south to British Columbia, Montana, Ontario, Quebec, and Maine (perhaps other parts of New England). Virtually accidental anywhere south of the above territory.


## BLACK GYRFALCON

*Falco rusticolus obsoletus* (Gmelin)
(Lat., *obsoletus*, worn out, obsolete, or dark)

RANGE: Northern North America from Point Barrow, Alaska, to Labrador. Winters south to Nova Scotia, Quebec, and Maine, casually to southern New England, New York, South Dakota, Kansas, Minnesota, and Ohio.


## ASIATIC GYRFALCON

*Falco rusticolus uralensis* (Sewertzov and Menzbier)
(Lat., *uralensis*, of the Urals [Mountains])

RANGE: Siberia to Kamchatka, Bering Sea islands, and coast of Alaska. Winters south to British Columbia and Washington.

HISTORY. These splendid birds are the largest of the family and by far the least known because of their extreme northern range. At home on the Arctic tundras and frowning cliffs of boreal islands, they seem to be all but avian phantoms, appearing and vanishing in ghostly silence. Very little is known about them. The Gyrfalcons, says Bent (1938), "have always been a very puzzling group . . . it now seems to be generally conceded that all the forms are races of one species *Falco rusticolus*." Regarding the chances of their being seen by the vast majority of bird students, Mr. Bent adds that the Gyrfalcons "are not likely to be seen within the U.S., except in winter." He might well have said *northern* U.S. The famous Hawk Mountain Sanctuary in the Kittatinny Mountains of eastern Pennsylvania seems as likely an area to watch for them in late fall as anywhere in the northeast. The race appearing there occasionally is *candicans* (White Gyrfalcon).

Field recognition is based on the usual falcon wing characters (long, narrow, and pointed): rapid wing beats, periods of sailing, and their large size. The speed attained by these birds is very great when pursuing prey, the latter often being caught and seized in the air. Both attacker and att. cked then fall to the ground where the Falcon proceeds with its meal. Open country is preferred; indeed, much of the range is treeless.

The Gyrfalcons are predominantly bird killers; their rarity in this country results in their being a negligible factor. They can hardly be said to "compete" with the vast majority of sportsmen and they cause insignificant loss to poultrymen. In relation to the over-all list of native birds, they simply constitute a biological control on overpopulation.

In the far north Ptarmigan, together with lemmings and Arctic hares, appear to bulk largely in the diet of the Gyrfalcons. During their fall and winter wanderings almost any sort of living prey is attacked—rabbits, rats, poultry, grouse, ducks, and shore birds.

The handsome appearance, dashing tactics of speed and courage, plus the aura of mystery which ever clings about these birds, all combine to stir admiration and respect in the most casual observer.

## PRAIRIE FALCON

*Falco mexicanus* (Schlegel)
(Lat., *mexicanus*, of Mexico)

LOCAL NAME: Mountain Hawk.

RECOGNITION: Adult: Gray or clay color above, with an indistinct grayish line over eye; cheeks light with faint "mustache" mark; underparts light, streaked or spotted with brownish; tail brown with narrow terminal white tip and numerous crossbars. Legs and feet yellow. Whole aspect of bird very pale.

Immature: Upperparts darker reddish-brown than adult; underparts more heavily streaked or spotted. Legs and feet bluish.

Length: Male, 17 to 18 inches; female, 18.5 to 20 inches; wingspread 40 to 42 inches.

NESTING: In niches or on ledges of cliffs, buttes, and mesas in arid desert country. Nest of sticks and other debris, lined with grass and feathers.

Eggs: 3 or 4. Reddish-buff, thickly sprinkled and spotted with chestnut. Measurement 2.05 × 1.60 inches.

RANGE: Breeds from British Columbia, southern Alberta, and Saskatchewan to eastern border of the Great Plains, southern Lower California, and Mexico. Largely resident where found. Casual east to Minnesota and Illinois.


HISTORY. The Prairie Falcon is another splendid representative of a superb family. In the wordage of the old falconers, it is a "noble" bird. Its entire aspect and the wildness and vastness of its chosen haunts combine to give an impression of primeval freedom that is associated with few other birds.

A dweller of western mesas, cliffs, canyons, and adjacent deserts, the bird is a master of aeronautics and an accomplished hunter. Resembling the Duck Hawk in much of its way of life and to some degree in appearance, it is a far paler bird, as desert forms are apt to be, and lacks the prominent "mustache" mark of its larger relative.

The Prairie Falcon shares a family trait by seeming to derive some sort of pleasure in hectoring other birds, often large species, with no effort to kill them. Curiously enough, the Great Blue Heron is a species often selected for such play tactics. Missing the larger bird only by inches in headlong "stoops" (dives), the Falcon will zoom upward, gain altitude, and plunge again and again, the heron meanwhile weaving and twisting in frantic efforts to escape. The diving tactics are, of course, those most used to secure prey, but the Prairie Falcon varies such spectacular procedure by indulging the very prosaic method of hopping over the ground in pursuit of grasshoppers.

Common perches are the very tops of trees, or jagged pinnacles of rock or cliff, commanding a wide sweep of country. Leading a wild and lonely life, and possessed of courage and fierceness, the Prairie Falcon has few natural enemies. Desperate encounters take place at times between individuals of the species, or two or three pairs, and occasionally combat may take place between this species and larger birds of prey.

Internal parasites have been known to infest some specimens; one such examined by E. D. Lumley and described by Bent (1938) was said to have been so afflicted that "The insides of the bird looked almost as if they had been sewed together with white thread." Man continues to be the greatest menace to this Falcon through prejudice or lack of information regarding its true status.

The Prairie Falcon, though essentially a "bird hawk," often preys upon rodents, which abound throughout its range. May (1935) quotes the late ornithologist-artist Allan Brooks as follows: "The Prairie Falcon . . . is noteworthy (for a falcon) in the pursuit of small mammals like ground squirrels, mormots and jack rabbits. In striking at these, it descends like a bullet at a long, low angle, and if the animal is missed it may richochet along the ground for some distance, striking again and again, a puff of dust marking each unsuccessful effort." This remarkable procedure is one I have never heard attributed to any other aerial hunter.

Examination of 40 stomachs of this Falcon from various parts of the range disclosed remains of birds and mammals in 13. It should be added that F. H. Fowler (1931) found, around three nests of the Prairie Falcon in California, remains of 26 rodents and 61 birds. There seems to be a definite seasonal variation in the diet, more birds and fewer mammals being taken in the winter.

# PEREGRINES

## DUCK HAWK

*Falco peregrinus anatum* (Bonaparte)
(Lat., *peregrinus*, wandering; *anatum*, of duck)

LOCAL NAMES: American Peregrine, Bullet Hawk.

RECOGNITION: Adult: Dark slaty blue above with dark bars, blackish on crown, cheeks, and "mustache" mark. Underparts white to cream buff, at times with a pinkish cast, barred on lower breast, sides, and abdomen with blackish-brown; upper breast and throat usually immaculate. Tail with about six narrow dark bands and broad subterminal blackish bar, tipped with white. Bill horn color; cere, toes, and tarsus (leg) yellow.

Immature: Similar to adult but upperparts dark brownish black with rusty edging on the feathers; underparts streaked with dark brown except for throat.

Length: Male 15 to 18 inches, wingspread 38 to 43 inches; female 18 to 20 inches, wingspread 43 to 46 inches.

NESTING: On ledges or in niches of cliffs, often under an overhanging projection. Sometimes in natural cavities of tall trees or on the stone sills and projections of skyscraper buildings. Hardly, if any, nesting material is used; but when it is, sticks, fur, feathers, and bits of rotten wood are utilized.

Eggs: 2 to 4, frequently the latter number. Ground color bright reddish buff, thickly sprinkled with chestnut and reddish brown: "the darkest, brightest marked, and most beautiful of Falcon eggs" (C. A. Reed, 1904). Average measurement 2.05×1.55 inches.

RANGE: Breeds from Norton Sound, Alaska, across to Baffin Island and west coast of central Greenland south to Lower California, central Mexico, Arizona, west Texas, Kansas, Missouri, Indiana, Pennsylvania, and Connecticut and south in the mountains (Blue Ridge) to western North Carolina and Tennessee. Winters from Vancouver Island through California and Colorado, southern midwestern and northeastern states, to the West Indies and Panama.

## PEALE'S FALCON

*Falco peregrinus peali* (Ridgway)
(Lat., *peali,* for Titian Peale)

RECOGNITION: Similar to *F. p. anatum* but much darker in general colora-
tion both in the adult and immature. This northwestern form of the Duck
Hawk breeds in the Queen Charlotte Islands, Aleutians, and Commanders.
Winters south to Oregon.

## PEREGRINE FALCON

*Falco peregrinus peregrinus* Tunstall

RANGE: This Falcon of Europe, similar to the Duck Hawk but more heavily
marked below and with the chest barred and spotted with brown or black, is
accidental in eastern Greenland. It has only been recorded there twice, and
one of these birds "closely resembled the Duck Hawk (F.C.R. Jourdain,
1933).
The Siberian Peregrine, *F.p. calidus* Latham, is accidental in Alaska.

HISTORY. This bird, to my mind, is the ultimate of the avian king-
dom, the epitome of the birds of prey. Embodying every quality
of that group and excelling in all except size, it is supreme among
birds.

Much of the great sport of falconry centers about this species, for
it was its Old World counterpart, the Peregrine Falcon, which was
so sought for and highly prized, its ownership limited to the nobility
and prohibited to any below the rank of earl. Duck Hawk seems a
rather prosaic term for the bird. Its specific name *peregrinus* means
"wandering," and Wandering Falcon would be far more appropriate. Nowhere common, it roams over a tremendous range and
is to land areas what that famous oceanic traveler, the Wandering
Albatross, is to the southern seas. By whatever name, this falcon
is a commanding figure in the natural world. It should draw admiration from sportsman, bird watcher, and nature student because of
its qualities so prized by humanity—fearlessness, power, speed,
and beauty.

In a superb description quoted by May (1935), the Duck Hawk is characterized by G. H. Thayer (1904) as "perhaps, the most highly specialized and superlatively well-developed flying organism on our planet today, combining in a marvelous degree the highest powers of speed and aerial adroitness with massive, warlike strength. A powerful, wild, majestic, independent bird, living on the choicest of clean, carnal food, plucked fresh from the air or the surface of the waters, rearing its young in the nooks of dangerous mountain cliffs, claiming all the atmosphere as its domain, and fearing neither beast that walks nor bird that flies, it is the very embodiment of noble rapacity and lonely freedom."

That the Duck Hawk *is* a bird hawk is a part of its life. The whole system of natural control seems to be embodied in its streamlined symmetry and way of life. It is built to kill and does so with consummate skill. The speed of the Duck Hawk has been measured by airplane pilots and found to be as much as 175 miles per hour. The method of attack is to gain a position slightly behind and over the intended prey, then to "stoop," or dive, upon it in a power thrust. The victim is stricken with the large, knobbed feet (Audubon called this Falcon the Great-footed Hawk), the result being that the back is broken or the target killed outright. The prey falls to the ground, to be followed and picked up by the falcon and carried to a convenient perch to be eaten. What the Falcon's speed may be at the greatest pitch of the stoop, no one knows, but it probably exceeds 200 miles per hour.

It seems at times that the Duck Hawk indulges in the spirit of play or enjoyment of its prowess. Time and again it dives with tremendous velocity upon other birds, only to swerve aside at the last possible fraction of a second and avoid them. I have seen it plunge at pigeons, shorebirds, and ducks and sheer away just at the moment of supposed impact, while the quarry wildly endeavored to dodge the dive. The Falcon appears to derive a sort of stimulus from the terrified efforts of the pursued to escape.

The Duck Hawk prefers open country—prairies, marshes, beaches, and wide meadows—not being found in forests or any wooded lands. Though nesting on cliffs below which mountain forests occur, it does its hunting in the air, striking down the victim in full flight. Curiously enough, it sometimes frequents the very center of large cities. Here it feeds on the hordes of pigeons, starlings, and English Sparrows which live in urban communities. I have seen this Falcon several times from Riverside Drive, New York, and about Radio City on Fifth Avenue. Nests have been found on ledges of skyscrapers in Philadelphia, the Traveler's Tower in Hartford, Connecticut, the Harkness Memorial tower of Yale University, and the Sun Life Insurance Building in Montreal. The Duck Hawk could hardly choose safer breeding sites if it were capable of thoughtful selection.

The variety of avian prey embraces a large range of subjects from warblers and vireos to grouse, herons, and ducks. Indicative of its preferences, the analysis of 102 stomachs from widely separated localities showed that remains of birds, of one species or another, were found in 81, and remnants of mammals and insects in 15. To the hunter, and the easily offended bird "lover," the statement of the Canadian ornithologist P. A. Taverner (1926) should be stressed. He says: "There should be enough game in the country to support so picturesque a character without arousing the jealousy of other hunters."

## APLOMADO FALCON

*Falco fusco-coerulescens septentrionalis* (Todd)
(Lat., *falco*, a falcon; *fusco*, brownish, *coerulescens*, being blue; *septentrionalis*, northern)

RECOGNITION: Adult: Upperparts bluish gray, barred across rump with whitish; secondaries edged with white and forming a band when bird is

**PEALE'S FALCON**

Upper figures, adult female and immature

**PEREGRINE FALCON**

Lower figure, adult female

**APLOMADO FALCON**

Adult perched, immature in flight

## PIGEON HAWK

Adult male perched, female or immature in flight

**SPARROW HAWK**

Male perched at left, female at right

## VULTURES, HARRIERS, ACCIPITERS

1, California Condor. 2, Turkey Vulture. 3, Black Vulture. 4, Marsh Hawk, adult male. 5, American Goshawk. 6, Sharp-shinned Hawk. 7, Cooper's Hawk.

## BUTEONINE HAWKS

1, Ferruginous Rough-leg. 2, American Rough-legged Hawk, light phase. 3, American Rough-legged Hawk, dark phase. 4, Red-tailed Hawk. 5, Broad-winged Hawk. 6, Short-tailed Hawk. 7, Red-shouldered Hawk, immature. 8, Red-shouldered Hawk, adult. 9, Mexican Goshawk. 10, Sennett's White-tailed Hawk. 11, Swainson's Hawk. 12, Zone-tailed Hawk. 13, Harris's Hawk. 14, Mexican Black Hawk.

## EAGLES, OSPREYS

1, American Golden Eagle, immature. 2, Bald Eagle, adult. 3, Bald Eagle, immature. 4, Gray Sea Eagle, adult. 5. American Osprey.

## KITES, FALCONS, CARACARAS

1, Everglade Kite, adult male. 2, White-tailed Kite. 3, Mississippi Kite.
4, Swallow-tailed Kite. 5, Prairie Falcon. 6, Gyrfalcon. 7, Duck Hawk.
8, American Sparrow Hawk, male. 9, Aplomado Falcon. 10, Pigeon Hawk.
11, Audubon's Caracara.

perched; tail increasingly dark toward tip, banded by 8 narrow white bars. Sides of head and "mustache" black; line over eye white, becoming tawny at back of head; throat and upper breast white; thighs and undertail coverts brownish-orange.

Immature: Pattern largely the same but colors duller and the back brownish; underparts buffy; breast streaked with dusky.

Length: Male 15 inches; female 17 to 18 inches; wingspread about 40 inches.

NESTING: A depressed platform of twigs lined with grasses, usually in the top of a Spanish bayonet (yucca) or mesquite at elevations of from 7 to 15 feet.

Eggs: 3 or 4. Creamy white, heavily speckled with small reddish brown spots, sometimes with splashes or blotches. Measurement 1.75 × 1.30 inches.

RANGE: Along the Mexican Border of Arizona, New Mexico, and Texas south through Mexico.

HISTORY. The status and range of this handsome little raptor coincides closely with those of the Zone-tailed Hawk. Both of them enter this country only in a narrow strip of the Southwest from western Arizona to Brownsville, Texas. In former years it appeared to be fairly common in several localities; this is no longer the case. In the Lower Rio Grande Valley about Brownsville it occurred regularly; but though I searched for it on many sanctuary inspections in that area from 1935 to 1941, I never succeeded in seeing it. Bent (1938) had a similar experience. It occurs in the Big Bend of Texas also, but in three trips to that region I again failed to find this Falcon. Any sight of it today would be a red-letter experience for the observer and shows how remiss we have been in not insisting long ago upon an effective protection program for it.

Falconlike, it takes birds now and then but to a lesser extent than some others of this regal tribe. Though not a great deal is known regarding its specific diet, enough is on record to prove that small birds, mammals, and insects play a part in it. Reptiles, such as snakes and lizards, figure as well.

It is somewhat larger than the Pigeon and Sparrow Hawks and

distinctive of plumage. It can be readily identified, for it looks like no other hawk. It shares the habit with others of hovering motionless in the air while sighting prey and also of being attracted to prairie or brush fires, where it darts through the smoke to snatch insects disturbed by the flames. The insects are then eaten in flight, in much the same manner common to the Kites and other Falcons. The Aplomado generally uses lower perches than its relatives and often alights on the ground; this behavior has perhaps been conditioned by the desert character of much of its range in this country.

It is problematical whether this interesting species can be encouraged to increase in numbers. Should the much desired "model hawk and owl law" become an actuality in the three states frequented by the Aplomado Falcon, much will be gained toward such an end. Certainly its presence in this country is in no way a detriment and its increase would be highly desirable from an aesthetic viewpoint.


# PIGEON HAWKS

## EASTERN PIGEON HAWK

*Falco columbarius columbarius* (Linnaeus)
(Lat., *columbarius*, dove keeper, referring to its bird killing)

LOCAL NAMES: Bullet Hawk, American Merlin, Pigeon Falcon.

RECOGNITION: Adult male: Upperparts slaty blue, feathers with black shafts; tail crossed with grayish bars and tipped with white. Underparts cream to ochraceous buff, heavily streaked with dark brown or blackish; throat white; "boots" reddish in old birds.

Female and Immature: Upperparts dark brown, neck streaked with lighter brown; three or four yellowish tail bars and a white tip. Underparts as in male.

Length: Male 10 to 10.50 inches; female 12 to 13.50 inches; wing-spread 24 to 26.50 inches.

NESTING: Site very variable. On ledges or niches of cliffs with little or no nesting material, or in hollows of trees and amid branches, when the nest is constructed of sticks, twigs, grass, and moss, lined with bark strippings and feathers. Occasionally old nests of other birds are utilized. Tree nests are usually in evergreens and elevations vary from about 8 to 15 feet.

Eggs: 4 to 6. Ground color brownish buff, heavily spotted with chestnut. (Eggs of the various races are all similar to *F. c. columbarius*.) Average measurement 1.50×1.22 inches.

RANGE: Breeds from limit of trees in eastern Canada south to Newfoundland, Nova Scotia, New Brunswick, northern Maine, Ontario and Michigan, and southern Manitoba west to eastern border of the Great Plains. Winters from the Gulf States south through eastern Mexico to Ecuador and northern Venezuela and the West Indies.


## WESTERN PIGEON HAWK

*Falco columbarius bendirei* (Swann)
(Lat., *bendirei*, for Major C. E. Bendire)

RECOGNITION: Similar to the Eastern Pigeon Hawk, but male lighter on upperparts; tail black, crossed with three gray-white bands. Female much like *F. c. richardsonii* but a darker shade of brown.

RANGE: Breeds from northwestern Alaska, Yukon, and Mackenzie to British Columbia, northwestern Alberta, and northern Saskatchewan south in the mountains to northern California. Winters south through California and New Mexico to the Cape region of Lower California and northwestern Mexico. Accidental in Louisiana, Florida, and North and South Carolina.


## BLACK PIGEON HAWK

*Falco columbarius suckleyi* (Ridgway)
(Lat., *suckleyi*, for G. Suckley)

RECOGNITION: A very dark form in which the dark areas are almost sooty black. The stripes of the underparts are broader and more sharply defined; throat often streaked rather than being unmarked.

RANGE: Breeds in western British Columbia and probably Vancouver Island. Winters in the coast region from British Columbia to northern California (uncommonly).

## RICHARDSON'S PIGEON HAWK

*Falco columbarius richardsonii* (Ridgway)
(Lat., *richardsonii*, for Sir John Richardson)

RECOGNITION: Much lighter than *F. c. columbarius*, resembling the Merlin of Europe *(F. a. aesalon)*. Upperparts of male pearl gray, the brown of all plumages having a bleached look in comparison with the Eastern Pigeon Hawk. Tail barred with 5 or 6 light bands (instead of 3 or 4); crown noticeably light.

RANGE: Breeds in the Great Plains region from southern Alberta and Saskatchewan to northern Montana and northwestern North Dakota. Winters south through Colorado, New Mexico, and west Texas to northwestern Mexico.

## MERLIN

*Falco aesalon aesalon* Tunstall
(Gr., *aesalon*, small hawk)

RANGE: The European Merlin is closely related to the American Pigeon Hawks. It has appeared once as an accidental wanderer in Greenland in 1875. Even that record is open to question, since the specimen may have been referable to the Iceland race of the Pigeon Hawk (*F. c. subaesalon*).

HISTORY. This little Falcon might well be described as a Duck Hawk in miniature. It embodies many if not all of that species' characteristics except size.

Closely related to the Merlins of Europe, just as the Duck Hawk is to the Peregrine Falcon, the Pigeon Hawks inhabit virtually all of Canada in the breeding range and extend through the United States, Mexico, and Central America into the northwest corner of South America in winter. They are not really common anywhere but fairly regular throughout the vast range. Like other Falcons, they are birds of open country, though wooded areas are not entirely avoided. When using tree perches, the Pigeon Hawk will often sit in among the foliage rather than on top of the tree or outside branches. Fence posts are used as perches in open prairie country and in south central Florida; such vantage points render it visible to visitors in the great reaches of the Kissimmee Prairie.

The speed of the Pigeon Hawk is reflected in one of its local names, Bullet Hawk. The small size of the bird probably increases the impression of speed, but the fact remains that it is a very fast bird. Its aerial ability and speed are illustrated by the fact that it occasionally takes swallows in full flight. Swallows are masterful fliers themselves and their turns, banks, and twists in the air enable them to escape most of the hawks. That the Pigeon Hawk can and does take not only swallows but those other aerial gymnasts, the bats, reflects a pitch of perfection in flying technique.

This little Falcon shows surprising tameness at times, allowing close approach; but perversely, at other times, takes flight when the observer, desiring a close look, is still some distance away. Its general appearance, both at rest and in the air, is strikingly like that of a pigeon, hence its name. Pigeons have been shot by those thinking they were firing at this Falcon, and vice versa.

The streaked underparts and lack of reddish plumage will differentiate the Pigeon Hawk from the far commoner Sparrow Hawk which it resembles in size. As for any confusion with the Duck Hawk (American Peregrine), the much smaller size of the Pigeon Hawk will always be diagnostic. The dark tail with its several crossbars is a good field mark as well as the slaty-blue upperparts.

Again, like others of its tribe, the Pigeon Hawk is, to quote May, "a confirmed bird-killer." Its small size limits depredations among larger domestic fowl, but it takes small chickens at times and thereby brings condemnation upon itself. During migrations, the Pigeon Hawk often accompanies flocks of shore birds, upon which it preys. Insectivorous birds also provide food for it; a score of species have figured in this falcon's diet. Small mammals and a considerable number of insects are eaten as well, so that birds do not, by any means, constitute the sole food. Dragonflies, beetles, grasshoppers, and caterpillars have been found in stomach contents. It is hard to begrudge this dashing little hawk anything it takes as a natural element of its existence.

# SPARROW HAWKS

## EASTERN SPARROW HAWK

*Falco sparverius sparverius* (Linnaeus)
(Lat., *sparverius*, pertaining to sparrows)

LOCAL NAME: Killy Hawk.

RECOGNITION: Adult male: Upperparts reddish-cinnamon, back barred with black; top of head blue with chestnut crown; throat and cheeks white; a black line extending below eye, another behind ear coverts, and 3 others on sides and back of neck; wing coverts and secondaries bluish spotted with black; rump and tail chestnut, latter with white tip and subterminal black band. Outer tail feathers black and white; breast tawny buff, belly whitish, spotted with blackish; cere, legs, and feet yellow.

Adult female: Head markings similar to male; back, wing coverts, secondaries, and tail duller, with narrow bars of blackish. Underparts streaked not spotted.

Immature: Resembles adult of same sex.

Length: Male 8.75 to 10.5 inches; female 9 to 12 inches; wingspread 20 to 24 inches.

NESTING: In natural cavities of trees or old woodpecker holes, occasionally in bird boxes, usually at considerable elevations from about 20 feet to the tops of tall trees. Little nest material is used.

Eggs: 4 to 6. Ground color cream buff, heavily sprinkled and spotted with reddish-brown, the markings sometimes almost obscuring the ground color. Average measurement 1.35 × 1.10 inches.

RANGE: Almost the whole of North America. Breeds from the Yukon across Canada to southern Quebec and Newfoundland south to northwest California, western Oregon, Colorado and east Texas, and the eastern Gulf states (except southern border of these) and Florida. Winters from southern British Columbia, middle states, and southern New England south through eastern Mexico and Panama. Accidental in Bermuda.

## DESERT SPARROW HAWK

*Falco sparverius phalaena* (Lesson)
(Gr., *phalaina*, a devouring monster)

A larger and paler bird than the Eastern Sparrow Hawk, with longer tail and larger crown patch, inhabiting the arid regions of southern New Mexico, Arizona, southern California, and Nevada south into Mexico and northern Lower California. Winters south to Guatemala.

## SAN LUCAS SPARROW HAWK

*Falco sparverius peninsularis* (Mearns)
(Lat., *peninsularis*, peninsular)

Smaller and paler than *F. s. sparverius*, with a lessening of the black markings and a larger bill, inhabiting southern Lower California.

## LITTLE SPARROW HAWK

*Falco sparverius paulus* (Howe and King)
(Lat., *paulus*, little)

Smaller and darker than Eastern Sparrow Hawk, with tail and wings shorter proportionately. Bill larger and red of underparts very dark. This form is resident in the Florida peninsula and southern portions of the Gulf states north to Central Alabama. (A form of the Sparrow Hawk, *F. S. guadalupensis* Bond, occurs on Guadalupe Island, Lower California.)

THE FALCONS     159

# KESTREL

*Falco tinniculus tinniculus* (Linnaeus)
(Lat., *tinniculus*, little bell-like note, referring to characteristic call)

A close European relative of the American Sparrow Hawks which has appeared in Greenland and Massachusetts. So closely related is it to our bird
that efforts are current to call our Sparrow Hawks Kestrels since they are
much more akin to it than to the European Sparrow Hawk, which is really
a counterpart to our Sharp-shinned Hawk.

HISTORY. The smallest and one of the handsomest of American
birds of prey is sadly misnamed. The term Sparrow Hawk is based
on the European bird of that name, which is a bird killer and
much more like our own Sharp-shinned Hawk both in appearance
and food preference The unfortunate misnomer leads many to conclude, naturally enough, that the American bird kills sparrows (and
other birds), which it rarely does. Insect Hawk, or even Killy
Hawk, would be far more appropriate terms for this beautiful
little falcon. It tends to live largely on insects, and the high-pitched
and characteristic call, which resembles the word "killy" or "tilly,"
is familiar to farm boy and city dweller alike the country over.

The Sparrow Hawk is probably the best-known American bird of
prey. It covers a tremendous range and is often seen in and about
towns and cities as well as remote and uninhabited regions, sometimes occupying bird boxes in suburban yards. It is mainly a bird
of open country and uses the most exposed and conspicuous kinds
of perches—telephone poles or wires, the topmost twigs of trees,
lightning rods, or dead stubs in open fields and pastures. From
these it sallies forth for its prey. The Sparrow Hawk is rather easily
tamed and makes a most attractive pet.

One of its most characteristic habits is a hunting technique of
hovering motionless in the air on rapidly beating wings as it scans
the ground. Though this behavior is common to both the Osprey and

Rough-legged Hawks—and occasionally Eagles—the great difference in size between all of them and the diminutive Sparrow Hawk is enough to distinguish the latter at once. The only bird of similar size which shares the habit is the Kingfisher, and the large bill, crested head, and other differences of the latter bird always make identification easy.

Sparrow Hawks are often seen circling and diving about the edge of grass or brush fires, flying in and out of the smoke to catch insects disturbed by the flames. I have seen as many as a dozen of these birds at a time so engaged.

In the eastern part of the country during winter, the Sparrow Hawk can perhaps be seen with greater frequency in Florida than anywhere else. It is astonishingly abundant there at that season. I have, at random, counted the birds perched on wires along the highways, fence posts, etc., in the Lake Okeechobee-Kissimmee Prairie region and the Keys, and found them to occur at the rate of one a mile over a span of 13 miles.

The food of the Sparrow Hawk consists very largely of insects, with small mammals next in preference. Stomach contents covering a wide range of localities and seasons are indicative if not conclusive. Of 427 examined, 416 contained remains of insects and small mammals, while 69 held bird remains.

In its bright colors, attractive way of life, and ease of observation, this little Falcon should appeal to any frequenter of the outdoors. It plays a prominent part in controlling forms of life which man spends vast sums to destroy and is an asset worthy of complete protection and encouragement.

# OWLS

ORDER *Strigiformes*

# x. The Owls

Mainly nocturnal birds of prey, the owls have large rounded heads and definite facial disks in which the large eyes center. The plumage is very soft and fluffy, the flight soundless. Some species have prominent ear tufts or "horns"; others lack them completely or possess such short ones as to be barely visible. The owls are principally inhabitants of woodlands, though some species frequent open country, and one nests in underground burrows.

FAMILY *Tytonidae*: BARN OWLS

## BARN OWL

*Tyto alba pratincola* (Bonaparte)
(Gr., *tyto*, owl; Lat., *alba*, white, *pratincola*, meadow inhabitant)

LOCAL NAMES: White Owl, Monkey-faced Owl.

RECOGNITION: Face white, with rim of cinnamon-buff feathers forming a heart-shaped disk; upperparts and wings ochraceous buff, mottled with gray; underparts cinnamon-buff, sometimes white, thinly speckled with dark brown. Wing lining white; legs long.
Length: 15 to 21 inches; wingspread 43 to 47 inches.

NESTING: In natural cavities of trees, niches of cliffs and canyons, hollows in the ground, barns, church steeples, deserted houses, ventilating shafts, ledges of buildings, waterway beacons, and watchtower beams.
Eggs: 5 to 7, occasionally up to 10 or 11. Ovate in shape and pure white. Incubation begins with first egg, rest laid at 2- to 3-day intervals, hence young are found in widely varying size. Measurement 1.70 × 1.30 inches.

RANGE: Resident from northern California, Colorado, Nebraska, southern Wisconsin, New York, and Connecticut south through the U.S. to southern

Mexico. Casual in Oregon, Minnesota, Michigan, Ontario, and central New England.

HISTORY. This queer-looking owl, more than any other, fulfills the conventional concept of a night bird. Though most people connect owls with darkness, the Barn Owl, a common species, is practically unknown to the great majority of citizens among which it dwells.

This species actually lives at times in the midst of cities, roosting and nesting in church steeples, factory attics, warehouses, and cornices of large buildings. When the bird is encountered great excitement usually prevails, for it is frequently supposed that a "new" species has appeared from some foreign land, or that a monkey and a bird have consorted to produce the queer apparition. The Barn Owl's face is rather remarkable in its heart-shaped outline, and there is an air of the ludicrous about its simian appearance—hence its local name of Monkey-faced Owl.

Although capable of seeing in broad daylight, this owl is seldom found abroad in such hours. I can recall few occasions when I have found it active by day. It is, of course, possible to watch the bird by day at its nest or perch. The most unusual observation I ever made was one of a Barn Owl which came aboard a steamship many miles off Cape Hatteras, N.C. This appearance took place at about 11 A.M., strong offshore winds prevailing at the time.

When darkness sets in this owl may often be seen in the headlight beams of motor cars, particularly in the Florida Keys, where the birds rise from the road shoulder or perch atop telephone poles. The paleness of the bird is very marked and at such times it appears quite ghostly.

A Barn Owl family is a remarkable exhibit in that it may consist of as many as seven to ten youngsters, all of different sizes. The variation is caused by the fact that the adults begin to incubate as soon as the first egg is laid, and as much as two weeks may elapse between the laying, and the hatching, of the first and last eggs. The immediate area of the nest (actually there is little if any nesting material) is unattractive to a degree, with the dismembered portions of rodents and other animal debris lying about. Such evidence, however, proves the value to agriculture from the activities of the owls in preying upon rodents.

The Barn Owl's plumage is silky in texture and light in general color. Aside from the much larger Snowy Owl, it is the palest of the family. The voice is sometimes startling in the extreme, for one of the notes is a sound which can be no better described than a demoniac shriek. Another is a rather weak call resembling the "peenck" of the Nighthawk. Clicking sounds are made by snapping the mandibles together.

This species appears to be rather susceptible to cold weather, perhaps because severe winter reduces the food supply and renders it unable to sustain vitality. As with the other owls, the flight is without any sound whatever. Open country is preferred in its hunting.

Owls have ever been objects of abhorrence and even fear on the part of the ignorant and superstitious. The Barn Owl is no exception and its presence in old buildings gives rise to "haunted houses." Many have been killed for no other reason than that they were owls, but even the briefest consideration of the diet is enough to show that real economic importance attaches to the species. Its principal food is rodents, which are often highly detrimental to food crops.

A pair of Barn Owls once nested in a tower of the Smithsonian Institution building in Washington. Dr. A. K. Fisher made a study of 200 pellets (disgorged indigestible portions of prey) collected about the nest and found a total of 454 mammal skulls therein. Among them were 225 meadow mice, 179 house mice, 20 rats, and 20 shrews—an amazing collection for a pair of owls living in the heart of America's capital city. The Barn Owls in California are known to feed largely on pocket gophers; those in the Southeast prefer cotton rats. It might be well to recall here that the cotton rat is the Number 1 enemy of the Bobwhite Quail in the southeastern U.S. Some birds are prey at times, but not often.

Nestling Barn Owls will eat their own weight in food every night. As many as 16 mice have been carried to one nest in 25 minutes, plus 3 gophers, a squirrel, and a rat. (T. G. Wheelock, 1904.)

Though typifying a nocturnal bird to most people, the Barn Owl has neither of two characteristics so often associated with owls: it does not possess "horns" and it does not "hoot."

FAMILY *Strigidae*: TYPICAL OWLS

## SCREECH OWLS

### EASTERN SCREECH OWL

*Otus asio naevius* (Gmelin)
(Lat., *otus*, a horned owl; *asio*, a horned owl; *naevius*, spotted)

LOCAL NAMES: Squinch Owl, Scritch Owl.

RECOGNITION: Two distinct color phases: Red phase: Upperparts rufous-cinnamon, streaked with black; underparts white, heavily marked with reddish. Gray phase: Upperparts brownish, streaked and barred with black and brown; underparts white, mottled with brown and streaked with blackish.

Head conspicuously "eared" or "horned"; iris yellow. Smallest of the eastern owls except the Saw-whet.

Length: 6.50 to 10 inches; wingspread 20 to 24 inches.

NESTING: Usually in hollows of trees but at times in old buildings or bird boxes. Nest material very scanty, a few feathers or hair.

Eggs: 5 to 8, pure white. Measurement 1.35 × 1.20 inches.

RANGE: Breeds from northeast Minnesota and New Brunswick south to northearn Kansas and northwestern South Carolina. Resident throughout breeding range.

BARN OWL

SCREECH OWL

Gray and red phases

Allan Brooks.

SNOWY OWL

**WHITNEY'S ELF OWL**

Female at left, male at right

BURROWING OWL

GREAT HORNED OWL

BARRED OWL

GREAT GREY OWL

SHORT-EARED OWL

LONG-EARED OWL

# SOUTHERN SCREECH OWL

*Otus asio asio* (Linnaeus)

RECOGNITION: Smaller than *O. a. naevius* and somewhat darker in plumage.

RANGE: Resident and breeds from Tennessee and southeast Virginia south to central Alabama and southern Georgia.


# FLORIDA SCREECH OWL

*Otus asio floridanus* (Ridgeway)
(Lat., *floridanus,* of Florida)

RECOGNITION: Gray phase similar to that of *O. a. naevius* but much smaller and all colors darker. Red phase very different in showing more reddish on the underparts, the breast almost uniformly colored and the red broken into broad crossbars.

RANGE: South Atlantic and Gulf States from east Texas to South Carolina north in Mississippi Valley to southern Illinois.


# TEXAS SCREECH OWL

*Otus asio mccali* (Cassin)
(Lat., *mccalli,* for Colonel George A. McCall)

RECOGNITION: Larger than *O. a. asio* but smaller than *O. a. naevius,* being paler than either. The gray phase more heavily mottled above. Red phase paler than *O. a. asio,* with reddish more prominent on underparts.

RANGE: Southern Texas north to Comal and Bexar Counties, west to Kinney County, and south into Tamaulipas and Nuevo Leon, Mexico.


# CALIFORNIA SCREECH OWL

*Otus asio bendirei* (Brewster)
(Lat., *bendirei,* for Major C. E. Bendire)

RECOGNITION: According to William Brewster, who described this race, "The chief difference is in the ground-color and markings of the plumage beneath." In *O. a. asio* the central line of breast and abdomen is nearly always immaculate; in this form it is as thickly barred and streaked as are the sides. The ear tufts average smaller. There is apparently no red phase but two variations of color, brown and gray.

RANGE: Coast region of California from about the Oregon line to the Bay Region (San Francisco).


## KENNICOTT'S SCREECH OWL

*Otus asio kennicotti* (Elliott)
(Lat., *kennicotti*, for Robert Kennicott)

RECOGNITION: A large dark form of the Pacific Northwest. More tawny brown above, the underparts rather strongly washed with pale cinnamon. Legs light tawny. Gray phase very dark.

RANGE: Resident from Sitka, Alaska, to northwest Washington.


## ROCKY MOUNTAIN SCREECH OWL

*Otus asio maxwelliae* (Ridgeway)
(Lat., *maxwelliae*, for Mrs. M. A. Maxwell)

RECOGNITION: Definitely larger and paler than *O. a. aikeni*, much lighter than any other form.

RANGE: Resident in the plains and foothills adjacent to eastern slope of the Rocky Mountains from western South Dakota and eastern Montana to central Colorado.


## MEXICAN SCREECH OWL

*Otus asio cineraceus* (Ridgeway)
(Lat., *cineraceus*, reddish)

RECOGNITION: Very smiliar to *O. a. aikeni*, but penciling on upper and under parts finer, those of underparts more numerous.

RANGE: Central Arizona, southern New Mexico, and west-central Texas to Lower California and Sonora, Mexico.


## AIKEN'S SCREECH OWL

*Otus asio aikeni* (Brewster)
Lat., *aikeni*, for Charles Aiken)

RECOGNITION: Similar to *O. a. cineraceus* but larger, upperparts more heavily mottled and with the mesial streaks wider and more strongly in contrast with the general color. It is smaller and darker than *O. a. maxwelliae*.

RANGE: The plains and foothills of eastern Colorado and Kansas north to northeast North Dakota and Minnesota, south to New Mexico, west-central Texas, and Durango, Mexico.


## MACFARLAND'S SCREECH OWL

*Otus asio macfarlanei* (Brewster)
(Lat., *macfarlanei*, for R. R. MacFarland)

RECOGNITION: This form is about the same size as *O. a. kennicotti* but resembles *O. a. bendirei* in color and markings. There are two color phases (gray and brown), but in the latter this race is not as dark as *kennicotti*.

RANGE: Resident in the interior of southern British Columbia, eastern Washington and Oregon, northern Idaho, and Montana to northeast California.


## HASBROUCK'S SCREECH OWL

*Otus asio hasbroucki* (Ridgway)
(Lat., *hasbroucki*, for E. M. Hasbrouck)

RECOGNITION: Very similar to *O. a. mccalli* but larger, darker, and with less buff-gray on upperparts; transverse bars on underparts broader and more numerous.

RANGE: Coastal Texas from Dallas County to Travis and Palo Pinto Counties (probably some adjacent).

## PASADENA SCREECH OWL

*Otus asio quercinus* (Grinnell)
(Lat., *quercinus*, of oak leaves)

RECOGNITION: Differs from *O. a. bendirei* in being paler. Absence or great reduction of reddish on chest and around facial rim is characteristic of this form. The gray phase is lighter and the brown phase duller than in the northern forms.

RANGE: Southern California west of the desert areas and on west slope of the Sierra Nevada north to the Mount Shasta region and Pacific side of northern Lower California.

## SAGUARO SCREECH OWL

*Otus asio gilmani* (Swarth)
(Lat., *gilmani*, for M. F. Gilman)

RECOGNITION: Very like *O. a. cineraceus* but smaller and paler.

RANGE: Lower Sonoran zone west of the Santa Rita and Santa Catalina Mountains.

## XANTUS'S SCREECH OWL

*Otus asio xantusi* (Brewster)
(Lat., *xantusi*, for John Xantus)

RECOGNITION: Similar to *O. a. cineraceus* but smaller, paler, and less reddish; abdomen and flanks whiter; undertail coverts nearly pure white and almost without mesial streaking.

RANGE: Southern portions of Lower California.

# SPOTTED SCREECH OWL

*Otus trichopsis aspersus* (Wagler)
(Gr., *trichopsis,* hairy-faced; Lat., *aspersus,* scattered)

RECOGNITION: Bent (1938) comments on this owl as follows: "On close examination, it is readily seen to be a distinct species and not a subspecies of *Otus asio.* This species is decidedly dichromatic, having very distinct gray and red phases, which is not true of any of the southwestern races of *Otus asio.*" The most conspicuous difference is the presence of large white spots on the lower hind neck as well as the scapulars and greater wing coverts, large black spots on underparts, and the well-developed bristly tips of the facial feathers.

RANGE: Southern Arizona mountains south through Mexico to Guatemala. Permanent resident in the Huachuca and Chiricahua Mountains of Arizona.


# FLAMMULATED SCREECH OWL

*Otus flammeolus flammeolus* (Kaup)
(Lat., *flammeolus,* flame color)

RECOGNITION: Smaller than the other Screech Owls, with short rounded ear tufts. Eyes dark chocolate brown. Variegated plumage of brown, silver gray, black, white, and cinnamon. Wide individual fluctuation exists between the extremes of red and gray phases, the variation seeming to be without geographic significance.

RANGE: Mountainous regions from southern British Columbia and Idaho south through Mexico to the higher areas of Guatemala.


# NEBRASKA SCREECH OWL

*Otus asio swenki* (Oberholser)
(Lat., *swenki,* for M.H. Swenk)

RANGE: This form of the Screech Owl occurs from southern Manitoba to western Oklahoma and central Kansas.

## SOUTHERN CALIFORNIA SCREECH OWL

> *Otus asio inyoensis* (Grinnell)
> (Lat., *inyoensis*, for Inyo, California)

RANGE: Southern California west of the deserts from Kern County to northwestern Baja, California.


## BANCROFT'S SCREECH OWL

> *Otus asio cardonensis* (Huey)
> (Lat., *cardonensis*, turning upon)

RANGE: Pacific slope of Baja, California, from Santa Domingo to El Rosario.

HISTORY. Although no owl could be described as well known to everybody, the Screech Owls would come as near to that classification as any of the family. The name is almost a household word, while the familiar notes are known far and wide, even if actual visual acquaintance is less common. The term "screech" is misleading. Whistling Owl would be better. The quavering, tremulous, and somewhat eerie call is anything but a screech, and the fact that it is heard in urban as well as suburban and rural communities makes these little owls known audibly to thousands of people who have never had a glimpse of them. The factor which keeps this owl from being better known by sight is its nocturnal way of life. Bird of darkness it is, and much of the superstition, fear, and misunderstanding connected with the owls arises from this fact. The call is often imitated by bird students to attract small birds within observational distance. Chickadees, Titmice, Kinglets, and Warblers often respond to the call and their excitement at such times gives an insight into their general reaction to the presence of the owl.

The Screech Owl exhibits two distinct color phases, gray and red. Individuals of both phases are to be found in the same nest, and the division appears to be about equal. The visual observation of this little owl is pretty much a matter of pure chance. Now and then the bird can be found roosting quietly in a patch of woodland or even in an isolated tree. As a general rule, the owl will be near the trunk of the tree rather than in the outside branches. When discovered, it usually elongates itself and reduces the eyes to mere slits, the "horns" being elevated to their greatest extent.

The type of habitat usually frequented is open woodland, edges of fields or farms, marshland borders, and swamplands. Occasionally, a bird may take up residence in a city garden or park and remain there for some time. For its size, this owl is remarkably aggressive and there are many instances of "attacks" on people intent on examining the nest, or even watching the birds at close range. I was once called by a neighbor to look at some small owls which had appeared on his front porch. It was about dusk when I walked through the yard and up the steps, when suddenly I was struck on the head by something which gashed my right ear. I went on up the steps to see three young Screech Owls ranged along the porch railing, but not before I had been swooped upon and touched by one or another of the adults who were in close attendance. This, I may add, is the one and only instance of any bird drawing blood from me. However, many such instances are in the literature.

The hearing of all owls is exceedingly acute; the slightest rustle in the grass or stir of a roosting bird will be heard. Their flight is absolutely soundless. I have crept up to a Screech Owl sitting atop a stump, while a companion held a flashlight on the bird, and been within a yard of it when it took off, yet not one whisper of sound came from the wings. Occasionally, when night hunting, these owls will swoop low in front of a motor car and thus be killed.

The food of the Screech Owl is widely diversified and the subject of controversy. A considerable number of small birds are taken (often English Sparrows) but small mammals such as mice figure largely as do insects. Again we must conclude that expediency and availability largely control this owl's food preferences. What may appear a detrimental influence in one locality may well be offset in another. Details of the diet are discussed at length by both Bent (1938) and Fisher (1893) and the student can draw personal conclusion therefrom.


# HORNED OWLS

## GREAT HORNED OWL

*Bubo virginianus virginianus* (Gmelin)
(Lat., *bubo*, a horned owl; *virginianus*, of Virginia)

LOCAL NAMES: Hoot Owl, Cat Owl.

RECOGNITION: Very large and heavy. Ear tufts conspicuous. Upperparts dark brown, finely mottled with buff and white; underparts buffy or whitish, barred with dark brown or black, these being lacking on center of upper breast, forming a wide white collar.
Length: 18 to 25 inches; wingspread, 49 to 57 inches.

NESTING: Though occasionally constructing a nest of its own, it is much more apt to use old nests of Crows, Hawks, or Eagles, adapting them to use. Has been known to occupy Bald Eagle nest while Eagle did also (Charles Broley, Florida). At times in crotches or hollows of trees, particularly in southern portions or range. In the West occasionally in niches of cliffs, or in cut banks and ancient Indian cliff dwellings. Nests on the ground have been found in Texas, Florida, and Newfoundland. A very early breeder throughout range.
Eggs: 1 to 5; 1 or 2 is usual number. Shell thick and coarsely granulated, rounded oval in shape, pure white. Measurement 2.25 × 1.85 inches.

RANGE: Breeds from Ontario, Quebec, and New Brunswick south to the Gulf Coast and through Florida. West to Wisconsin, eastern Minnesota, southeastern South Dakota, eastern Kansas, Oklahoma, and Texas.

# WESTERN HORNED OWL

*Bubo virginianus pallescens* (Stone)
(Lat., *pallescens,* being pale)

RECOGNITION: This is a paler form than the typical Great Horned Owl but essentially similar in habits, behavior, and nesting.

RANGE: Northeastern California (Lassen County), Idaho, and Utah east to New Mexico and central Texas, south to Mojave Desert and into northern Mexico.


# ARCTIC HORNED OWL

*Bubo virginianus wapacuthu* (Gmelin)
(*Wapacuthu,* Indian name for this bird)

RECOGNITION: A very pale form of *B. v. virginianus,* nearly as white at times as the Snowy Owl. Legs and feet pure white. Intergrades with *B. v. occidentalis* in extreme southern portion of range.

RANGE: Breeds from northern timbered areas of Canada south to central Alberta, Saskatchewan, Manitoba, and northern Ontario. Occurs occasionally in winter from British Columbia to Wisconsin.


# DUSKY HORNED OWL

*Bubo virginianus saturatus* (Ridgway)
(Lat., *saturatus,* full rich color)

RECOGNITION: The darkest of the horned owls.

RANGE: Heavy, humid forests of the Pacific Coast region from northern California, Oregon, and Washington through British Columbia to Alaska.


# PACIFIC HORNED OWL

*Bubo virginianus pacificus* (Cassin)
(Lat., *pacificus,* of the Pacific)

RECOGNITION: This is the horned owl of most of California, where it occurs in wooded river bottoms, foothill ravines, and mountain forests up to 7,000 feet (except the northwest humid coast strip).

## LABRADOR HORNED OWL

*Bubo virginianus heterocnemis* (Oberholser)
(Lat., *heterocnemis*, different, a legging)

RECOGNITION: A large dark race with larger bill and paler posterior lower parts than *B. v. saturatus*.

RANGE: It ranges from the northern portions of Labrador and Newfoundland south through New England to Connecticut.

## MONTANA HORNED OWL

*Bubo virginianus occidentalis* (Stone)
(Lat., *occidentalis*, of the west)

RECOGNITION: This is the horned owl of the Yellowstone Park as well as other areas east and west of that part of the Rocky Mountains.

RANGE: It breeds from southeast Oregon, central Alberta, Montana, South Dakota, and Minnesota south to Iowa, Kansas, Wyoming, and northeastern California.

(The St. Michael Horned Owl [*B. v. algistus*], the Northwest Horned Owl [*B. v. lagophorus*], and races which occur in different parts of Alaska, the latter penetrating southward to British Columbia, northern Oregon, and Idaho. The Dwarf Horned Owl is not included here since it inhabits the southern part of Lower California and is not to be seen in this country.)

HISTORY. This big owl is probably the ultimate in fierceness among North American birds of prey. Though eagles are usually so considered, the Great Horned Owl far exceeds the Bald Eagle in fearlessness and defense of its nest. The great naturalist Ernest Thompson Seton wrote of this species: ". . . all that I have seen of them—

their untamable ferocity . . . their magnificent bearing; their objection to carrion, and strictly carnivorous tastes—would make me rank these winged tigers among the most pronounced and savage of the birds of prey."

Any species inhabiting such a tremendous range as does this owl naturally exhibits differences in plumage and other characteristics which, in various climates, have resulted in its being separated into several geographical races (just as the Screech Owl has). The behavior and general habits of all the races, however, are similar.

The Great Horned Owl is a bird of heavy woodlands and, at times, scattered patches of trees, but extensive agricultural development will cause its disappearance from formerly inhabited range. Seclusion and adequate food are essential to its existence.

The soundless flight combines both grace and power. Periods of sailing intervene between wing beats, and it threads its way amid forest growth with easy precision. It has been known to indulge in soaring flight in broad daylight, much as do the Buteo hawks, and it hunts by day as well as night.

A very powerful bird, it has been known to fly off with a steel trap attached to its foot, having broken the chain which held the trap. In one remarkable instance, noted by J. J. Murray of Lexington, Virginia, one of these owls was caught successively by two pole traps and flew away with first one, then the other, a foot in each. It managed to live and subsist for weeks thereafter and only succumbed when one of the trap chains caught on a fence and the owl was killed. Such a record argues for extraordinary stamina, endurance, and ability to survive.

Attacks on human intruders of its domestic life are fairly numerous. A. C. Bent was once nearly knocked out of a tree by "terrific blows" from this owl and suffered ugly scalp wounds. Samuel A. Grimes, the well-known bird photographer of Jacksonville, Florida, reports in *The Album of Southern Birds* that he had a similar experience, despite being equipped with a heavy wire-mesh helmet. So determined were the attacks upon him by both owls of the pair whose nest he was attempting to photograph that he was obliged to retreat from the scene.

Captive Great Horns are seldom tractable and, unless taken when less than two weeks old, do not, except in rare instances, lose their sullen, ferocious dispositions. When I was connected with the Charleston Museum we had a young Great Horned Owl which had been raised from a youngster. On one occasion, when a medical student attempted to handle the bird, it sunk its talons in his hand so deeply and tenaciously that the tendons of the leg had to be cut before the grip was loosened. The bird appears to be as ferocious toward its own kind as any other; this is illustrated by a quotation from Bent (1938) of an experience of Otto Widmann (1907), who had a captive Great Horned Owl which lived for 29 years. This bird one day suddenly set upon its mate of seven years, killed, and partially devoured it.

The food habits of this owl have been, and still are, a subject of endless controversy, dissension, and argument. One could hardly sum up the matter better than by quoting what Bent (1938) has to say about it: "The great horned owl is a ravenous feeder on a great variety of animal life, and a very generous provider for its hungry young; almost any living creature that walks, crawls, flies, or swims, except the larger mammals, is its legitimate prey; it is not at all particular as to what it kills for food and will take what is most available and most easily caught. It is so powerful and aggressive that it can attack and kill surprisingly large mammals or birds."

Among mammals, particularly in the West, the rabbit seems to be this owl's chief food. The bird has often been reputed to prey upon skunks, and many specimens brought to taxidermists have the odor of that animal on them. Many nests have been impregnated with the skunk scent. The owl has also been known to attack and kill porcupines, specimens having been taken with quills imbedded in various parts of the body. Reversing the usual concept of cats killing birds, the Great Horned Owl has been known to kill house cats. Rats, mice, gophers, and other such mammals often figure in the food, as do birds. The species taken by this owl cover a wide range, from birds as large as Swans and Geese down to Sparrows. Decoy ducks are preyed upon, as well as such wildfowl kept in uncovered pens, while Grouse and Turkeys are taken at times here and there in the range of the owl. Individual Great Horned Owls develop a taste for poultry in certain localities. Illustrative of its wide diet was an experience of Major Charles Bendire in 1892. He examined a nest of this owl which contained the following items brought in as food for the young: "a mouse, a young muskrat, two eels, four bullheads (catfish), a woodcock, four ruffed grouse, one rabbit and eleven rats." The total food at this nest when weighed was found to be nearly 18 pounds!

Dr. Paul Errington of Iowa State College concludes an article on the Great Horned Owl in *Audubon Magazine* (May-June, 1954) with this sage bit of conservation philosophy:

My suggestion to people who can enjoy outdoor values is that they consider the Horned Owl as neither a feathered friend nor as a feathered fiend, but simply as a very distinctive and very interesting part of our outdoor heritage. As a wild species, it gives no allegiance to man nor owes him any, which is true of all wild species so long as they are wild—and which is as it should be. So far as I am concerned, the Horned Owl, by living its own life in its own way, has repaid me for any competition it has given me for "my" rabbits and other game (as a veteran hunter, I could claim losses as logically as anyone), for its depredations upon my poultry (our lakeside "old home farm" in South Dakota had perhaps "average" losses when I lived there), and for a fairly impressive collection of talon scars that I carry on my person. I would say that, even from a man-centered point of view, the Horned Owl belongs in our natural out-of-doors wherever its activities are not too much in conflict with human interests and that persecuting it at random, merely because killing it may be legal or customary to do so, is a mistake.

Leaving out the witchcraft and man's favorite label of "destructiveness," we have in the Horned Owl a superb predatory type, one of glorious wildness in a time when wildness becomes more and more priceless with each new encroachment of human populations and technology on what wildness we have left.

The hooting of the Horned Owl in a winter evening is reassurance to me that real wildness still exists, and I am thankful to live where I can hear it. Far from being a dismal or menacing sound, it has for me a freedom and beauty to make the air sing.

The voice of this great owl is one of its outstanding characteristics. It is a "hoot" owl indeed. Deep and resonant, the notes have much carrying power. One of them resembles the sound "whoo-hoo-whoo-hoo," repeated; in other words, four syllables, given twice. There is also a kind of bark, given under excitement, "whoo-hoo-hoo, whah, whah." Veritable screams are said to be uttered at times, but these I have never heard, although I have lived within the range of this owl all my life. Another of its calls has been likened to crazy laughter. All these are difficult to translate into words. I have heard young Great Horned Owls, recently out of the nest, give a peculiar moaning "mew" sound which did not seem to come from a bird at all but was definitely traced to this species. The sounds carried for a long distance and the bird was only located with difficulty.

When it is seen at reasonably close range, there should never be any trouble in identifying this species. The white throat is easily noticeable as are the pronounced ear tufts (horns), which show well when the bird is on the nest incubating. The large size is indicative; the yellow eyes also help. When the owl is in flight the large head and very short neck are good field characters.

## SNOWY OWL

*Nyctea scandiaca* (Linnaeus)
(Gr., *nyctea*, nocturnal; Lat., *scandiaca*, of Scandinavia)

LOCAL NAME: White Owl.

RECOGNITION: Plumage entirely white, or barred and spotted with dark brown in varying degrees from light to heavy. No ear tufts (horns). Iris yellow.

Length: 20 to 27 inches; wingspread 38 to 60 inches.

NESTING: Usually on the ground atop a hillock or rise in tundra country, sometimes on cliff ledges. Nest material, if any, very scanty, a little moss and a few feathers.

Eggs: 5 to 8. Nearly spherical, pure or creamy white, shell somewhat granulated and with no gloss. Measurement 2.25 × 1.80 inches.

RANGE: Breeds from northern Alaska and Greenland south to central western Alaska across Canada to northern Quebec. Winters from southern Alaska and Labrador south to northern U.S. Appears occasionally southward into middle states and rarely farther, then becoming accidental.

HISTORY. Fresh from the azaleas and camellias which were in full flower at my home in Charleston, in mid-March I had gone to Saginaw Bay, Michigan, on a bird-collecting trip. Great ice cakes were piled along the beach and a glittering berg loomed offshore amid the steel-blue waters. The scene was strange and somewhat formidable to a young Carolina bird student. As I walked along that unfamiliar shoreline I suddenly saw, atop an ice cake, a huge white round-headed bird staring at me with black and yellow eyes. Then it rose and flew soundlessly away, a rabbit dangling in its talons. It was a Snowy Owl.

This great ghostly wanderer from the Arctic tundras is one of the most impressive of the owls. No sight of it is easily forgotten.

The Snowy Owl's name matches its chosen haunts, the far north, and it sometimes remains there throughout the year, making no southern flight. It lives in perfectly open tundra country to the very shores of the Arctic sea, able to exist by reason of its ability at hunting and its resistance to cold and storm. The appearance of this great owl in the United States, however, cannot be called a rare occurrence, for veritable invasions take place on occasion— usually at four-year intervals. These coincide with a low cycle of the rodent population in the north, when the owl is forced southward to find sufficient food—not because of severe weather, for "Ookpikjuak," as the Eskimos call this owl, is well able to stand the cold. In these visitations it does not often penetrate below the middle tier of states, but sporadic records exist as far south as the Carolinas and even Florida. Comparatively few of the beautiful wanderers return north after these southern flights, since they seem irresistible targets for trigger-happy people. Trophy after trophy finds its way to taxidermist shops; since the owl appears in towns and cities at times, the opportunity to shoot one is widespread, although this owl is now protected in many states.

The Snowy Owl is a powerful bird, fast in flight and with much strength in its formidable talons. Rabbits, skunks, and even small foxes are killed by it, as well as many rodents. In its normal range the lemming seems to be a mainstay of its diet, but other small mammals and birds as well as fish figure in it too. Because of the intermittent character of its visits to this country, it is hardly an important economic factor. At times, poultry and game birds are prey of this owl. The diet of many of the birds of prey is a matter of expediency and, as stated by Bent (1938), "the economic status of the Snowy Owl depends on circumstances."

There is much variation in the brown markings of this owl; some specimens are heavily barred and spotted while others are practically pure white. The flight is noiseless, strong and steady, the upstroke of the wings being rather jerky. Periods of sailing occur between wingbeats. It does considerable hunting in daylight and uses conspicuous perches from which to watch for prey. The flesh of the Snowy Owl is used as food by the Eskimos, who are said to be very fond of it. In this respect it appears to differ from all other members of the family.

When a bill to remove protection from the Snowy Owl was before the New York Legislature in 1951 (it was defeated), two statements were made that seem worthy of repeating here. In concluding its testimony on behalf of the owl, the National Audubon Society stated: "It is not a question of whether predatory birds, such as the Snowy Owl, occasionally eat game birds and mammals, but rather it is a question of whether or not that predation is significant. Professional wildlife managers are now quite well agreed that predation is not an important factor in limiting game-bird populations except in certain isolated situations. We do know, on the other hand, that predatory species, such as hawks, owls, foxes, wolves, etc., are essential to the health of the wildlife community, and that they are the first line of defense against the tendency of the eaters of plants, such as rodents, to increase disproportionately."

Dr. Arthur A. Allen, professor of ornithology at Cornell University, made this statement: "Even our more familiar birds, like Robins and Waxwings and Catbirds, are occasionally destructive, and yet no enlightened person today questions the desirability of protecting them; and I feel equally certain that were the people of this state as familiar with the Snowy Owl as they are with the Robin, they would demand its continued protection. Few of us are privileged to travel to the barren grounds of the far north to see this bird on its native heath, and so we naturally welcome the occasions when scarcity of rodents in the north drives it southward."

## HAWK OWL

*Surnia ulula caparoch* (Muller)
(Gr., *surnia*, a bird of evil omen, owl; *ulula*, a name for a screech owl; *caparoch*, Eskimo name of an owl)

RECOGNITION: Upperparts brownish, spotted with white; underparts regularly barred with brown; crown and back of neck spotted with white and black, a patch of black or dark brown on each side of the hind neck. Tail rounded and barred with indistinct whitish bands. Head without ear tufts.
Length: 14.75 to 17.50 inches; wingspread 31 to 33 inches.

NESTING: In natural hollows or atop broken stubs of trees, usually spruce, and in old woodpecker holes. Elevation varies from about 5 to 30 or more feet. Sometimes in old crows' nests. Nest, when made by the owls, of sticks and moss, lined with feathers.

Eggs: 3 to 7, occasionally as many as 9. Pure white, the shell smooth and without much gloss. Measurement 1.50 × 1.20 inches.

RANGE: Breeds in northern portions of North America from Alaska to southern Quebec and Labrador and central Newfoundland. Wanders south in winter to parts of northern United States. Not regularly migratory. (The Siberian Hawk Owl [*S. u. ulula*] is of accidental occurrence in Alaska.)

HISTORY. This bird was appropriately named, for it combines habits and appearance of both hawks and owls. While it has the soundless flight of the owls, it shows considerable speed and grace aloft, and its posture when perched is very suggestive of a hawk. Furthermore, much of its hunting is done by day.

The Hawk Owl is a boreal species, ranging over much of Canada and penetrating into northern Alaska. Bent (1938) quotes A. D. Henderson of Belvedere, Alberta, who had found this owl breeding near there, as follows: "To the north lies the great northern forest of poplars, spruce, pine, birch, tamarac, willow, alder, etc., which, broken only by smaller prairies, burns and muskegs, extends north to the limit of trees. . . . The particular haunt of the Hawk Owl is in the muskegs and here they can usually be found perched on some dead stub watching for prey."

Ernest T. Seton, often quoted by Bent, says (1890) that "The most striking feature in the behavior of the hawk owl is its tameness, boldness, or utter lack of fear, perhaps largely due to its lack of familiarity with human beings. It has repeatedly shown no concern when closely approached and has even been captured by human hands."

This owl defends its nest vigorously and has been known to attack and strike human intruders, another evidence of the reliability of Seton's (and others') observations.

Though varying with the seasons, the main food of this owl is small mammal life, such as lemmings, mice, and ground squirrels during summer, and ptarmigan in winter. Small birds and insects are taken at times. Henderson (1919) says that mice are a staple diet and that he once saw a Hawk Owl carrying an ermine (weasel). He wanted the specimen himself and attempted to frighten the owl into dropping it, but was unsuccessful.

The voice of the Hawk Owl has been described as a kind of trilling whistle, at least on the part of the male. Varied though other notes may be, all seem to be musical. Of medium size, rounded head with no ear tufts, and long, graduated tail, which is often twitched up and down when the bird is perched, the Hawk Owl is recognizable at once. The transverse barring of the underparts and rather short, pointed falconlike wings aid further in its identification. The species is seldom seen in this country, but occasionally penetrates the northern tier of states. Few field observers can expect to see it except on a northern expedition.

# PYGMY OWLS

## ROCKY MOUNTAIN PYGMY OWL

*Glaucidium gnoma pinicola* (Nelson)
(Gr., *glaucidium*, a kind of owl; *gnoma*, the knowing one; Lat., *pinicola*, pine dweller)

RECOGNITION: Very small, about size of Bluebird. Upperparts slaty gray-brown; underparts white, striped with black; sides of breast brownish, spotted with pale brown. Tail dark crossed with whitish bands. Crown speckled or dotted with white. Head round with no "horns."
Length: 6.50 to 7.50 inches; wingspread 14.50 to 15.50 inches.

NESTING: In abandoned Woodpecker holes or natural cavities of trees, usually from 8 to 30 feet above ground.
Eggs: Nearly spherical, pure white. Measurement 1.00×.90 in.

RANGE: Breeds and is largely resident throughout the Rocky Mountain region from Montana south to southern Arizona and southern California north to northern British Columbia except on coast.


## VANCOUVER PYGMY OWL

*Glaucidium gnoma swarthi* (Grinnell)
(Lat., *swarthi*, for H. S. Swarth)

RECOGNITION: Generally darker throughout than *G. g. californicum*. Larger and much darker than *G. g. pinicola*.

RANGE: Vancouver Island and adjacent mainland of British Columbia.


## COAST PYGMY OWL

*Glaucidium gnoma grinnelli* (Ridgway)
(Lat., *grinnelli*, for Joseph Grinnell)

RECOGNITION: Browner than *G. g. californicum*, varying from deep snuff to Verona brown.

RANGE: Humid coast area of California north from Monterey to Oregon, Washington, British Columbia (except Vancouver Island), and southeastern Alaska.


## FERRUGINOUS PYGMY OWL

*Glaucidium brasilianum cactorum* (Van Rossem)
(Lat., *brasilianum*, of Brazil; *cactorum*, cactus)

RECOGNITION: This is a northern race of a South American species. It was first secured in this country by Major Charles Bendire in January, 1872, near Tucson, Arizona. It is lighter in color and smaller in size than the typical race which occurs in Brazil, having two color phases and an intermediate phase. These are known as a gray-brown with white tail bands, a gray-brown with rufous tail bars, and a definitely red phase.

NESTING: Similar to the other Pygmy Owls, but the eggs of this race differ from those of the California Pygmy Owl in being more granulated. The general habits and behavior do not vary to any extent from the other Pygmy Owls.

RANGE: In the United States the range of this form is the Lower Rio Grande Valley and southern Arizona. (The Mexican Pygmy Owl, *G. g. gnoma* Wagler, occurs in the Huachuca and Santa Rita Mountains of southern Arizona.)

HISTORY. This species is a tiny creature for an owl, though not as small as the Elf Owl. Bent (1938) says that it is hardly as large as a Bluebird and not as large as a Robin. Aside from its diminutive proportions, it has an unowllike characteristic of frequently holding the tail at a definite angle from the body.

Living in the forested mountains of the Far West, the Pygmy Owl makes up for its lack of size by remarkably fearless determined hunting technique. It is the terror of small birdlife and its hunting, carried on largely, if not entirely, by day, is performed with quickness and dash. Fear and excitement are instant reactions on the part of small birds when they discover this owl perched. The tiny raptor is then at once mobbed by a growing crowd of Chickadees, Juncos, Warblers, Kinglets, and Jays. It is often possible to find a Pygmy Owl by watching or following one of these mob scenes closely.

The flight of the Pygmy is more like that of the Shrikes than that of other owls. It is not soundless either, since there are no soft wing linings. This owl is apt to indulge in short flights with a pause between. Abroad by day, it is often overlooked in some areas where it occurs, since few observers think of looking for an owl by daylight, much less one the size of a bluebird.

Sharing another Shrike characteristic, the Pygmy Owl sometimes stores unfinished remains of a meal in niches of tree limbs or other hiding places, presumably for future use. However, since fresh prey, such as mice, is nearly always readily available, the bird apparently does not return often to cached remains. During the nesting season the Pygmy Owl preys upon many small birds, but for the remaining nine months of the year subsists mainly upon insects, small mammals, lizards, and snakes. It does little harm to poultry, being too small to cope with any but very young specimens.

The voice of this little owl is mellow and musical. One of the calls is a series of notes given at even pitch, several fairly rapid, then a distinct pause before the following note and a longer interval before the last. It is easy to imitate and will often attract the owl to the human caller. The owl itself gives the call with a ventriloquial quality which makes it hard to locate. Another note is simply a kind of trill.

# ELF OWLS

## WHITNEY'S ELF OWL

*Microathene whitneyi whitneyi* (Cooper)
(Gr., *Microathene*, little Athena, goddess of wisdom; Lat., *whitneyi*, for Professor J. D. Whitney)

RECOGNITION: Smallest of American owls. Upperparts gray-brown, finely mottled with darker shades and faintly speckled with pale reddish; tail brownish, crossed by 5 or 6 narrow bands, or pale brown or reddish. Eyebrows and chin white. Underparts white with lengthwise markings of reddish brown.

Length: 5.50 to 6.75 inches; wingspread 14.25 to 15.25 inches.

NESTING: Usually in old Woodpecker holes (often Gila and Gilded Flicker) excavated in saguaro cactus. Elevations vary from 10 to 30 feet. Also in hollows of sycamore trees (Santa Catalina and Santa Rita Mts., Arizona) at elevations from 4,800 to 6,100 feet above sea level. Cottonwood trees have also been used and, in the Texas Big Bend (Chisos Mts.), stalks of the maguey (agave).

Eggs: 3 to 5. Oval in shape and pure white, the shell finely granulated with or without medium gloss. Measurement 1.02 × .90 inches.

RANGE: Southern Arizona, southwest New Mexico, Sonora (Mexico), and along a restricted area of the lower Colorado River in southeast California.

# TEXAS ELF OWL

*Micropallas whitneyi idonea* (Ridgway)
(Lat., *idonea*, capable)

The type of this race of the Elf Owl was taken by Frank B. Armstrong near Hidalgo, Texas, in April, 1889. The range is far removed from the birds frequenting Arizona (*M. w. whitneyi*) and is only the Lower Rio Grande Valley southward into Mexico. (Sanford's Elf Owl, *M. W. sanfordi* [Ridgway], is a race inhabiting lower California.)

HISTORY. This tiny bird is a veritable owl miniature. It is, to my mind, the most attractive of the family for that reason.

The Elf Owl, aptly named, is a westerner—southwesterner in fact, for its home is in the southern desert regions of Arizona, Texas, and southeastern California. Although connected almost inseparably, in its Arizona range, with the giant saguaro cactus, it is not, as Bent (1938) points out, confined to that growth. He quotes Berry Campbell (1934) as saying that he found this tiny owl in "upper Sonoran grassland" amid a growth of live oak, walnut, and sycamore. A. J. van Rossem (1936) has found elf owls in cottonwood groves on the Santa Cruz River at a spot 14 miles from the nearest saguaro stands. However, the principal habitats are the hot lower Sonoran plains in southern Arizona. Typical growth of its range is mesquite, creosote bush, and various cacti, such as cholla and others, among which the huge saguaros tower. I have tapped upon scores of these great cacti in the endeavor to induce this little bird to appear. A pair had been using a tall maguey stalk just behind the headquarters of the Big Bend National Park in the Chicos Mountains of Texas one summer when I was visiting there, but despite frequent visits I could never get the inhabitants to show themselves.

The Elf Owl is decidedly nocturnal and remains more or less immobile in daylight. When evening approaches it becomes active and often flies about the vicinity of campfires, probably because of the presence of insects attracted by the light.

The call is heard more frequently in early evening and about daylight, though uttered at times through the night. One of the notes has been likened to that of the Bluebird, another is like the word "chirp," and there is a two-syllabled call hard to render into words.

The food of this little owl appears to consist almost entirely of insects, such as grasshoppers, beetles, caterpillars, crickets, and centipedes. Captive specimens have been offered birds and refused them. It is obvious that an owl no larger than a sparrow would hardly be able to prey upon any form of birdlife, native or domestic. By the same token, the bird is not capable of preying upon small mammals, but its insect-eating habits render it an economic asset. It surely deserves and should receive complete protection and encouragement not only from that standpoint but also because it is one of the most interesting birds of this country.

No trouble should be encountered in identifying this bird of prey. Smaller than the Pygmy Owl, it has no rival in this regard and is far less apt to be seen by day than its nearest rival in size.

## BURROWING OWLS

### WESTERN BURROWING OWL

*Speotyto cunicularia hypugaea* (Bonaparte)
(Gr., *speotyto*, a cave owl; Lat., *cunicularia*, a burrower; Gr., *hypugaea*, underground)

LOCAL NAMES: Ground Owl, Prairie Owl.

RECOGNITION: Upperparts earth drab with white and buffy spots and bars; underparts whitish gray, heavily marked with snuff brown. About Screech Owl size but with long legs and no ear tufts.
Length: 9 to 11 inches; wingspread 22.50 to 23.50 inches.

NESTING: In abandoned holes of burrowing rodents such as prairie dogs, the nest being no more than a few wisps of grass at the end of the burrow, lined with cow dung.

Eggs: 5 to 8, occasionally more, nearly spherical and pure white. Measurement 1.25 × 1.00 inches.

RANGE: Plains regions from British Columbia to Guatemala, east to the Dakotas, Nebraska, Kansas, and west Texas. West to California in southern portions.

## FLORIDA BURROWING OWL

*Speotyto cunicularia floridana* (Ridgway)
(Lat., *floridana*, of Florida)

LOCAL NAMES: Ground Owl, Howdy Owl.

RECOGNITION: Similar to *S. c. hypugaea* but smaller and paler.
Length: 8.50 to 9 inches.

NESTING: Since there are no burrowing rodents in the range of this form, it excavates its own burrows. These are from 6 to 8 feet in length, with a curve at the end of which is an enlarged chamber in which the eggs are laid. The eggs are the same as those of the western form in shape and size. Occasionally found in loose colonies.

RANGE: This eastern form is found in the central prairie regions of Florida from St. Cloud and the Tampa region south to Sarasota (west coast) and east to Lake Okeechobee. Occasionally about the Miami region and, in winter, rarely into the Keys.

HISTORY. This remarkable owl is one of the strangest of the family. An owl living underground and there bringing up its young seems an anomaly, but such is the case with this long-legged "earless" bird. Two forms of it occur in this country, one living on the western plains and over to the Pacific coast, the other on the great open reaches of the Florida prairies and in scattered areas elsewhere in that state.

The name of this owl is well chosen. In the West, it often uses the abandoned holes of such rodents as the prairie dog, but such is not the case in Florida where it excavates its own burrow. The burrow is dug with the feet, both sexes working at it, and after descending at quite an angle for two feet or so, leveling off parallel with the surface. Usually there is a curve before the nesting chamber. A mound of white sand marks the mouth of the burrow, and one or the other of the owls is often standing guard thereon. They see well by day.

The manner of flight is undulating and not sustained for great distances. Upon alighting, the owl will frequently bob and curtsy in a most comical fashion, this habit having given rise to the local name in Florida of Howdy Owl.

The usual note is a sort of chuckle and is given when the nesting area is invaded. I have never heard any other sound from the bird except a sort of "cac-cac," though it is said to utter a cooing note during courtship. The old fable about burrowing owls living in the same burrow with prairie dogs and rattlesnakes persists, but it has no foundation in fact.

Occasionally, when hunting, this owl will indulge in a hovering flight like that of the Sparrowhawk or Kingfisher. Essentially terrestrial, it alights at times on fence posts and low bushes, and I have seen it on telephone wires. Close approach is often possible, particularly in a car. Some burrows are dug on shoulders of prairie roads, and it is sometimes possible to lean from a car window and look down a hole. By slowly circling a nesting pair in a jeep or station wagon, I have come to within 15 feet of both birds.

Some persecution of these owls is carried on by ranchers and cowboys who consider the burrows a detriment to both cattle and horses on the ground that a broken leg may result from the animals' stepping into a burrow. This is probably an unusual occurrence, but the idea persists and owls are still destroyed for this reason.

The food of the Burrowing Owl covers a wide range. In the West it takes many ground squirrels (spermophiles), mice, gophers, crickets, and grasshoppers as well as lizards, small snakes, beetles, dragonflies, scorpions, and centipedes. About burrows in Florida I have often found the remains of frogs and crayfish as well as many kinds of insects. Birds are sometimes preyed upon by this owl, and I have found remnants of Meadowlarks, Killdeer, and, once, a Wilson's Snipe, the latter seeming a strange item in view of its swift and erratic flight. The owl may have pounced upon the Snipe on the ground. It seems certain that birds figure to a minimum extent, however, and that the insects secured result in advantage to grasslands and pastures. This bird is a voracious feeder; the amount of food consumed in a day, or brought to the young, will equal the owl's weight. Protection and encouragement of the Burrowing Owl should be extended wherever the bird occurs.

# BARRED OWLS

## NORTHERN BARRED OWL

*Strix varia varia* (Barton)
(Lat., *strix*, a screech owl, *varia*, different)

LOCAL NAMES: Hoot Owl, Swamp Owl.

RECOGNITION: Upperparts dark brown, widely barred with white or buffy; underparts white or grayish-white, the breast with *transverse* dark bars and the abdomen with *lengthwise* streaks. Head large and round with no ear tufts (horns). Legs feathered, including the toes. Eyes dark brown to black.
Length: 17 to 24 inches; wingspread 40 to 50 inches.

NESTING: Either in deserted Hawk or Crow nests, or the hollows and crotches of large trees and tops of palm stubs. Pairs have returned to the same nest or immediate vicinity for as long as 20 to 25 years.
Eggs: 2 to 4, usually 2. Pure white with no gloss, rounded-oval in shape. Measurement 1.95 × 1.65 inches.

RANGE: Breeds and is resident from Saskatchewan and Newfoundland south to northern Arkansas and North Carolina, casually farther south.

# FLORIDA BARRED OWL

*Strix varia georgica* (Latham)
(Lat., *georgica,* of Georgia)

RECOGNITION: Similar to *S. v. varia* but with *unfeathered* toes. Plumage darker.

RANGE: Resident in southeastern United States from eastern Texas, Arkansas, and northern Alabama southward (particularly common in Florida).


# TEXAS BARRED OWL

*Strix varia helveola* (Bangs)
(Lat., *helveola,* yellowish)

RECOGNITION: Similar to *S. v. varia* and *S. v. georgica* but much paler, with upperparts yellowish-cinnamon, the light markings more conspicuous.

RANGE: South-central Texas from eastern border of Edward's Plateau (Bexar County) to the coast.


# CALIFORNIA SPOTTED OWL

*Strix occidentalis occidentalis* (Xantus)
(Lat., *occidentalis,* of the west)

RECOGNITION: This western representative of the Barred Owl differs from the eastern form in having the bars on head and back broken into rounded, irregular spots. The lower parts are *transversely* barred, much as is the breast of the eastern Barred Owl.

(This form has an interesting history. It was discovered by Xantus, one of the early naturalists of the Far West, near Fort Tejon, California (southern Sierra Nevada Mountains), in early 1858. It was not seen again until 14 years later when Major Bendire found it in southern Arizona. Although seen on occasions since, it has never been established as common anywhere. Though it is seldom seen owing to its nocturnal tendencies, it may be more common than is generally believed.)

RANGE: Southern British Columbia south to northern Lower California, east to New Mexico and central Mexico.

(Other races of the Barred Owl have been described, but the A.O.U. Checklist (1931) recognizes only the following: northern Spotted Owl [*S. v. caurina*] and the Mexican Spotted Owl [*S. v. lucida*]. In all races the nesting, eggs, and behavior are similar to the type species.)


HISTORY. The Barred Owl is probably the best known of the larger owls, for it is common throughout its wide range. Much of the hunting done by this owl is about farms and open country. It occasionally ventures into towns and cities in search of prey and is, I feel sure from much observation, the owl most often killed along highways by motor vehicles.

Its normal habitat is woodland, usually rather dense. From evergreen forests of the north to the palm hammocks of Florida, and from the damp tree growth of the Pacific Northwest to the Arizona highlands, this owl is encountered in one or another of its geographical races. In many parts of its range it is essentially a dweller of swamps, hence one of its local names. In the experience of many field students it is the owl more frequently found in daylight, when roosting, than either the Great Horned or the Screech Owls. I have often heard its deep-toned hooting at midday in the South Atlantic region and particularly in the swamps and hammocks of the Kissimmee Prairie region of Florida in winter.

This owl is rather noisy and has a varied vocabulary. The usual call might well be rendered as "hoo-hoo-too-hoo-oo," with sometimes an addition of "whah-whah-whah-oo" and often an "aw" sound at the termination of the call. Now and then veritable yells or screams, like those of a panther, are uttered and are unearthly and startling. Some writers have rendered the hooting in the words "who-cooks-for-you" and, in the case of the Florida Barred Owl (resident in southeastern U.S.), "who-cooks-for-you-*all.*" The notes of the Barred Owl are easily imitated and the species can often be attracted in this way.

This owl, like many others, can see perfectly well in daylight. The hearing is very keen, the slightest rustle being instantly noted. On numerous occasions this owl has flown close over my head (sometimes all but touching it) while uttering the "squeak" (kissing the back of the hand), a sound intended to attract birds. The method of flight is light and airy, with rather slow wingbeats and periods of sailing, and without any sound whatever.

Crows give this owl, as well as others, much annoyance. Indeed, the presence of an owl can often be detected by the clamor and activity of Crows which circle, dive, and perch about it, bedeviling and profaning it with all the intensity of which they are capable.

The economic importance of the Barred Owl is clearly proved. It consumes great numbers of rodents and comparatively few native birds and poultry. Occasionally, it exhibits cannibalism, remains of other owls having been found in the stomach contents of this species. E. H. Forbush (1927) once found remains of a Long-eared Owl in a Barred Owl's stomach, and in the stomach of the Long-ear were remnants of a Screech Owl! A captive Barred Owl has been known to eat 19 mice one after the other. This owl hunts now and then in broad daylight.

# GREAT GRAY OWL

*Strix nebulosa nebulosa* (Forster)
(Lat., *nebulosa*, cloudy [gray])

RECOGNITION: Largest of the owls. Uniform dusky gray-brown and grayish-white. Head very large, round, and out of proportion to rest of body. No ear tufts; eyes yellow.

Length: 25 to 30 inches; wingspread 54 to 60 inches.

NESTING: Nest usually in poplar or spruce woods, constructed of sticks and lined with feathers or hair. Elevation varies from 12 feet to the tops of tall trees.

Eggs: 2 to 5, usually 3. Dull white with granulated shell but no gloss. Rather more oval than other owl eggs. Measurement 2.15 × 1.70 inches.

RANGE: Timbered areas of central and western Canada from Hudson's Bay to Alaska and Pacific coast. South in mountains to central California (Yosemite). Has been known to breed in northern Minnesota. Occasional in winter in northern United States.

HISTORY. The Great Gray is one of the least known of American owls, since it has a far northern range, largely uninhabited. Much the same thing could be said about the Snowy Owl's range, but that bird does enter the U.S. in numbers at times, while the Great Gray does not. In over-all measurement the latter is the largest of the owls, but neither in weight nor size of body is it equal to the Snowy and Great Horned Owls. Actually, it is little larger than the Barred Owl, but the very large head, long wings and tail, and loose, fluffy plumage make it appear bigger than it really is. The weight varies from about one and a half to two and a half pounds.

In this country the Great Gray is occasionally encountered in northern and central New England, Michigan, Wisconsin, and Minnesota in winter, and in California as far as the Yosemite Valley, where it may nest. Few field students have been fortunate enough to see it. By those who have, it is said to be either tame or stupid, for it often allows close approach, sometimes having been caught in the hand, probably because it is unfamiliar with human beings.

In the far north it hunts by day, but in the more southern portions of the range it is more crepuscular and nocturnal. The generally dark gray plumage, lack of "horns," rather small yellow eyes, and great size will at once distinguish it from all other owls.

The calls are a musical whistle, not unlike that of the Screech Owl, and deep-toned hooting.

The food of this owl is largely small mammals, such as the young of rabbits, squirrels, rats, and mice. Small birds are occasionally preyed upon. At times the Great Gray retaliates upon its family's tormentor, the Crow, for it has been seen with a specimen of this bird, partly eaten, in its talons. Mammals as large as adult red squirrels have been found in the stomach of this owl. It is too rare in this country to figure as an economic factor, but certainly can be regarded as an interesting member of the interdependent wildlife community.

# LONG-EARED OWL

*Asiootus wilsonianus* (Lesson)
(Lat., *Asio*, horned owl; *otus*, horned owl; *wilsonianus*, for Alexander Wilson)

LOCAL NAME: Hoot Owl.

RECOGNITION: Upperparts blackish brown, mottled with whitish and buff; underparts white or buffy, streaked with dark brown, most heavily on breast, narrowly barred on lower abdomen.
Length: 13 to 16 inches; wingspread about 30 inches.

NESTING: Usually an adaptation of an old Crow, Hawk, or Squirrel nest, mostly in coniferous trees. In the western range, old Magpie nests are used. Occasionally it nests on the ground.
Eggs: 4 to 8, pure white. Measurement 1.55 × 1.35 inches.

RANGE: Breeds from central British Columbia, southern Mackenzie, and Newfoundland south to northern Lower California and Virginia. Winters from southern British Columbia, across to Massachusetts, and south to Louisiana and Florida (rarely) and central Mexico.

HISTORY. This owl occupies a tremendous range, nearly the whole of the United States and wooded portions of Canada. Apparently, sufficient timber to afford it concealment during daylight and furnish nesting sites is all that the species requires. Nonetheless, it is practically unknown by the great majority of people among whom it lives, both because of its nocturnal habits and its motionless roosting by day in some well-foliaged tree. This owl is a much commoner bird in many localities than actual observance of it indicates.

Much of its behavior is at variance with that of other species. It indulges, for instance, in the "broken wing" act, an attempt to lead an intruder away from the nest by feigning injury. This, according to Bent (1938), is unique among the birds of prey, in his experience. W. L. Dawson (1923) gives an interesting account of how he was duped by one of these owls near a nest:

The male parent had delivered himself of his quaint objurgations and had retired from the scene in disgust. The female had caterwauled and cajoled and exploded and entreated by turns, all in vain. . . . All of a sudden the owl left her perch, flew to some distance and pounced upon the ground, where she could not well be seen . . . upon the instant of the pounce, arose the piercing cries of a creature in distress, and I, supposing that the bird in anger had fallen upon a harmless Flicker which I knew dwelt in that neck of the woods, scrambled down instanter and hurried forward. The prompt binoculars revealed neither Flicker nor mouse. There was nothing whatever in the owl's talons. The victor and victim were one and the same, and I was the dupe. Yet so completely was the play carried out that the bird fluttered her wings and trod vigorously, with a rocking motion, as though sinking her claws deeply into a victim.

The Long-eared, like some other owls, will attempt to avoid observation by flattening its plumage and elongating itself to a remarkable degree. The "ears" are held vertically and close together and the whole posture, variegated plumage, and complete immobility result in the bird looking like a branch or piece of bark.

The flight of this owl is very buoyant and, of course, noiseless, giving the impression of a giant butterfly. The prey is usually secured by a quick pounce. The food, though exhibiting a seasonal range, is, on a yearly average, from 80 to 90 per cent rodents of a character injurious to agriculture. Bent (1938) states that in many examinations he made of the records of its diet, he could find but one record of a Quail having been taken, and two Ruffed Grouse. There was no indication whatever of attack on domestic poultry.

Early evening and morning as well as moonlight nights are the bird's favorite hunting times. Occasionally wintering groups of Long-eared Owls are encountered, varying in number from three or four individuals to as many as fifty. These will remain in or about a patch of woodland for weeks or even months at a time, and are probably composed of family groups.

This species is definitely one of the "hoot" owls, but its vocabulary is not thus limited. One of the calls has been rendered as "quoo-oo-oo," being both mellow and musical. When the bird is excited about the nest, such effects as "wack-wack" are produced with certain mewing notes and others all but approaching shrieks. For much of the year it is a very silent bird.


## SHORT-EARED OWL

*Asio flammeus flammeus* (Pontoppidan)
(Lat., *flammeus*, flame-colored)

LOCAL NAMES: Marsh Owl, Bog Owl.

RECOGNITION: Tawny buff above to buffy white below, with conspicuous dark streakings. "Ears" very short. Flight soundless and somewhat moth-like. A dark patch on upper surface of wings with a lighter one underneath.
  Length: 13.75 to 17 inches; wingspread about 43 inches.

NESTING: On the ground sometimes in a slight depression, rarely in a clump of bushes or tall grass. Heavy grass and sticks compose the nest, the interior lined with finer grass and feathers.
  Eggs: 5 to 7, white. Measurement 1.55 × 1.25 inches.

RANGE: Cosmopolitan. Breeds from about the 69th parallel in North America, Europe, and Asia. In former years from Alaska and Baffin Island south to New Jersey, Ohio, Kansas, Utah, and central California. Winters from central New England, southern Ontario, and Montana south to the Gulf Coast, Florida, and Guatemala.

HISTORY. While all owls are rather unfamiliar to most people, this species is even less known than others. Yet it is possible to see it in daylight, for it is often abroad before dusk. However, the bird cannot be expected in woodlands, for it is a species of open country, frequenting the great salt marshes of the South Atlantic seaboard, as well as the grassy meadows, dunes, and beaches of New England and prairies of the West. The Short-eared Owl is a wide ranger, and the interior of continents appear to be as attractive to it as coastal areas.

Small groups are often found together in winter, three to six and even more individuals at times. Some ornithologists consider these as family units remaining together in migration and subsequently in wintering grounds. On the southward flight in fall, this owl is sometimes encountered at sea, voyaging like a huge moth amid the immensity of waters. I have noted it nearly a hundred miles east of Cape Hatteras. In one such instance a Short-eared Owl followed the ship for miles directly over the wake, and once came aboard and perched for some time on a stay.

The hunting method of this owl is reminiscent of the Marsh Hawk in that it flies slowly along over the grasstops, searching for any movement of an unwary rodent. The flight, like that of the other owls, is without sound, and when dusk arrives the dark, round-headed form floating silently through the air is startlingly like a gigantic moth. The "ears" or feather tufts of the head are often so inconspicuous as to be invisible in flight and, at times hard to find even when the specimen is in hand.

The tremendous hemispheric range of the species appears to embrace a definite food preference regardless of national boundary lines. The principal food is small mammals, particularly mice. Examination of stomach contents, analysis of pellets, and numerous individual observations point to the fact that about 75 per cent of this owl's diet is composed of mice. Striking illustrations of such a diet are widespread. For instance, in Iowa, Beal found nothing but mice in stomachs examined. The owls taken were secured in a grove "swarming with small birds." Park, in western New York, found a similar condition there. An Oregon specimen (Fort Klamath) contained the skulls of ten shrews. Brenniger of Kansas reports "mice, insects and ground squirrels" in his findings. Tomkins collected 68 pellets from a roosting place near the mouth of the Savannah River (South Carolina-Georgia) and found remains of 96 mice, 4 rats, and 38 birds.

In Fisher's authoritative analysis (1893) the statement is made that "It is quite exceptional for this owl to feed upon birds." Poultry and game birds are practically never molested. There are, of course, exceptions to the rule in regard to general birdlife. Brewster, in Massachusetts, once found a small colony of these owls preying upon nesting Terns at Muskegat Island.

British, Scottish, and Scandinavian biologists have found that this owl attends the migratory movements of certain small mammals, such as the lemming, when they reach one of their population "highs," and constitutes a definite control upon them.

What few birds are taken by the Short-eared Owl are usually ground dwellers, such as the Sparrows, marsh birds of the Blackbird family, and occasionally small shore birds. It is indeed difficult to understand why anyone would, on knowledge of the facts, be anything but enthusiastic in advocating complete protection for this very valuable bird.


## RICHARDSON'S OWL

*Aegolius funerea richardsoni* (Bonaparte)
(Gr., *Aegolius*, a kind of screech owl; Lat., *funerea*, funereal, *richardsoni*, for Sir John Richardson)

RECOGNITION: Upperparts dark brownish; crown with white spots and large white spots on back. Bill yellow; outer edge of facial disk blackish.
    Length: 9 to 12 inches; wingspread 22 to 26 inches.

NESTING: In old Woodpecker holes (Flicker or Pileated) or natural cavities. At northern limits of range, sometimes in old nests of Thrushes or Rusty Blackbird, in bush growth or stunted trees.
    Eggs: 3 to 7, usually 4 or 5. Oval in shape, pure white, the shell smooth with little gloss. Measurement 1.25 × 1.05 inches.

RANGE: Northern North America. Breeds from Alaska east to Quebec and rarely New Brunswick, southern Manitoba, central Alberta, and northern British Columbia. Not regularly migratory.

HISTORY. This little owl, far northern in distribution, resembles the much better known Saw-whet Owl of this country. It lives in the wooded regions of Canada and only visits the United States in winter in the northern tier of states. It has been known to nest as far south as Grand Manan, New Brunswick, and has been seen in summer in the Green Mountains of Vermont, so it may nest in the extreme Northeast of this country. However, it is so boreal in usual range that few observers ever have a chance to see the bird, and it does not figure in any economic sense.

Richardson's Owl seems to fulfill the popular, and erroneous, opinion that these birds see poorly in daylight. The Eskimos, who know it quite well, call it the Blind Owl, but Bent (1938) believes that "unfamiliarity with man accounts for its apparent tameness" rather than any inability to see in daytime. Other far northern birds show the same quality of tameness.

This little owl often remains in sub-Arctic country throughout the winter, and one phase of its behavior may help in explaining such procedure. It takes up quarters now and then in abandoned igloos, and when flushed therefrom appears bewildered and confused. In Northern Maine it has been found frequenting barns and old buildings, living in such places during very severe weather.

The voice of Richardson's Owl has been compared to the peal of a high-pitched bell, or the dripping of water. The Montagne Indians of the north country call it the "water-dropping bird." Again, the note has been likened to the human voice, "a single melancholy note" (Dall, quoted by Bent, 1938).

This owl is somewhat larger than the Saw-whet, which it generally resembles. However, a reasonably good look at it will disclose the yellow bill, in contrast to the black beak of the Saw-whet, and the very dark color of the outer edge of the facial disk. White *spots*, rather than streaks, appear on top of the head and large, rounded white spots on the back.

The food of Richardson's Owl is composed mainly of small rodents and insects. Captive specimens have evidenced a decided preference for mice over birds. It is largely nocturnal in habit and hunting.

## TENGMALM'S OWL

*Aeogolius funerea magnus* (Buturlin)
(Lat., *magnus*, large)

The following is quoted from *Life Histories of North American Birds of Prey* (Bent, 1938):

This is not the well-known Tengmalm's Owl of Europe, but another of those light-colored races of Siberian birds that has occurred as a straggler in North American territory. Dr. Barton W. Evermann (1913) reported, under the name of *Cryptoglaux funerea funerea*, the capture of a Tengmalm's Owl on St. Paul Island, in the Pribilof group, on January 26, 1911. It was caught alive in the village by a native and brought to Dr. Walter L. Hahn. "The stomach was empty save for a few hairs. This is the first record for America of this interesting little owl."

The specimen is now in the United States National Museum and has been referred to the race of Tengmalm's Owl which inhabits the Kamchatka and Kolyma districts in northeastern Siberia. . . .

# SAW-WHET OWL

*Aegolius acadius acadius* (Gmelin)
(Lat., *acadius,* of Acadia)

RECOGNITION: Smallest of the eastern owls.

Adult: Dark brown above, streaked and spotted with white; underparts white, with wide brown stripes. Head rounded, with no ear tufts.

Immature: Forehead, eye stripe, sides of throat, and chin white; remaining upperparts, throat, and breast dark brownish; abdomen cinnamon-buff.

Length: 7.50 to 8 inches; wingspread 18 to 22 inches.

NESTING: Usually in hollows of trees or old woodpecker holes, at varying elevations. Very occasionally in bird boxes (limb with hole) erected in woodlands.

Eggs: 4 to 7. Oval in shape, shell smooth with little or no gloss, pure white. Measurement 1.20×1.00 inches.

RANGE: Temperate Canada and northern United States. Breeds sparingly south to Massachusetts and New York and across to Oregon, south in the mountains to southern Mexico. Wanders in winter as far south as South Carolina, Georgia, and Louisiana.


# QUEEN CHARLOTTE OWL

*Aegolius acadica brooksi* (Fleming)
(Lat., *brooksi,* for Major Allan Brooks)

A very dark race of the Saw-whet Owl resident on the Queen Charlotte Islands. There is no reason to believe that it differs materially in habit, nesting, and food preferences from *A. a. acadius.*

HISTORY. This is the smallest owl of the eastern U.S. and Canada and one of the most attractive. Its outstanding character is its tameness, and in consequence it is relatively well known. The Saw-whet can often be approached to within a few feet, or even inches, and has been frequently caught in the hands. It is a woodland owl and prefers dark coniferous forests rather than open growth. A low ranger, the bird avoids treetop elevations and roosts close to the ground or a few feet above it.

The flight is compared to that of the Woodcock by both Fisher (1893) and Bent (1938), being erratic and wavering. Like that of other owls, the flight is without any sound. Small birds often discover this owl roosting and their excited clamor enables an observer to detect the bird when otherwise it would have been easily missed.

Another character of this owl is responsible for its name, which arises from the peculiar note. This note is usually delivered in threes, the sound being much like the filing of a saw. There are other calls as well, one being a four-syllabled note and another a kind of sharp whistle. Audubon mentions a bell-like call with a ventriloquial quality which probably has to do with courtship.

While largely resident where found, the Saw-whet Owl does migrate. In some years it turns up in the most unexpected places and also suffers considerable mortality—just why, no one has ever clearly ascertained. Dead birds have been found in barns, old buildings of various kinds, and even in the woods. It hardly seems that cold alone would be responsible; probably a combination of severe weather and a failure of food supply result in a lowering of the birds' vitality.

Though definitely smaller than the Screech Owl the Saw-whet can be further recognized by the lack of "horns" and the very round head. It is more like the much rarer Richardson's Owl, but differs from the latter in having a black, instead of yellow, bill. There is no black border to the facial disk and the crown is streaked, not spotted as in Richardson's Owl.

The food of the Saw-whet is mainly mice, young rats, squirrels, chipmunks, and bats. A few small birds are taken occasionally, such as sparrows, juncos, and warblers and now and then insects. Too small to take poultry or game birds, it presents no problem to anyone, and in the aggregate, consuming quantities of small rodents, constitutes another control upon their populations.

# Appendix

## State and Provincial Laws Relating to Bird Protection
### BY KENNETH D. MORRISON

In 1899, the year *Bird-Lore* was founded, only five states offered any legal protection to the eagles, hawks, and owls. By 1949 some 30 states protected all of these species except the so-called "bird hawks" and the horned owl.

Since the 1949 survey, a number of changes have been made in state bird protection laws. Also, it was realized that nowhere was a compendium of such laws available in printed form. Hence the present survey has been broadened to include the status of all wild birds, not just the Raptores.

It is interesting to note that eight states have laws that are inconsistent with the federal protection afforded by the Migratory Bird Treaty Act. The worst offender is Texas, which lists five species of birds that receive federal protection as unprotected in that state.

As of the present survey, only seven states fail to protect any hawks or owls. They are Arkansas, Georgia, Maine, Maryland, New Mexico, Oklahoma, and Virginia. Rhode Island protects only the Osprey.

It is becoming more generally recognized that it is ecologically unsound to classify any species of hawk and owl, or any other form of wildlife, as "harmful." Each has its function in maintaining a healthy wildlife community. Control should only be attempted in individual cases where specific damage to property is involved.

Most state laws still exempt from protection the *Accipiters* or so-called Bird Hawks, as well as Horned Owls, thus reflecting the outmoded idea that bird species should be categorically classified as "harmful" or "beneficial." As a result, little attempt has been made to enforce the laws because, generally speaking, the only people who can distinguish between the protected and unprotected hawks are those who would not shoot them anyway. If a violator is brought into court, he usually pleads that he thought he was shooting an unprotected hawk. Almost invariably the case is dropped.

In order to reduce the slaughter of hawks that are funneled into narrow flight lanes during migration and to partly compensate for their unprotected status under the migratory bird treaties, some conservationists have proposed that all hawks be protected during migrations (September 1 to November 30, and March 1 to April 30) by an Act of Congress. Hawks would continue to be under the jurisdiction of state laws except during migrations. It is believed that at present there would be too much opposition to any proposal to protect all hawks at all times by federal law.

Probably the most significant development since the 1949 survey is the enactment of laws in Connecticut, Michigan, and Indiana that protect all species of hawks and owls except when doing specific damage. The Michigan and Indiana statutes specify that hawks or owls doing damage may only be destroyed by the farmer or landowner on the land he owns or occupies. It is gratifying to report that organizations and individuals in a number of states and Canadian provinces are working to secure the enactment of similar "model laws."

The revised single-sheet circular, *Hawks Are Your Friends,* which contains flight silhouettes of hawks on one side and information about their food habits and ecology on the other, is being widely distributed by local and state Audubon Societies and other conservation groups. Each state conservation department was also invited to participate in the distribution of these inexpensive hawk circulars. Twenty-four of them responded and are now circulating the educational leaflets under their own imprint. It is indeed encouraging that so many state agencies are co-operating with the National Audubon Society in its program to increase public understanding of the value and functions of the birds of prey in the wildlife community.

Most birds are protected by federal law. For a complete list of the species thus protected, write to the Fish and Wildlife Service, Washington 25, D. C., and request a copy of Bulletin 327, *Birds Protected by Federal Law.* Since federal law takes precedence over state law, we have indicated with an asterisk those birds in the following list which are federally protected. Even though specifically listed as unprotected by a state, they may not legally be killed in view of their protection by federal law. (Although blackbirds are listed as federally protected, the regulations concerning taking of them under certain conditions have been so liberalized that it seems pointless to asterisk them.) As you will note, most states extend protection to all but a few species of birds—thus legally saving from harm various hawks, owls, pelicans, ibises, and other species which unfortunately do not enjoy federal protection.

Species listed below are not protected by state laws. All other species *not* listed are protected. The birds of prey are grouped together at the head of each list following.

ALABAMA Chicken Hawk, Cooper's Hawk, Sharp-shinned Hawk, Great Horned Owl, Blue Darter, English Sparrow, Crow, Starling, Buzzard.

ARIZONA Cooper's Hawk, Goshawk, Osprey, Sharp-shinned Hawk, Great Horned Owl, English Sparrow, Crow, Raven, Starling, Magpie, Sapsucker*, Cowbird, Grackle, Kingfisher, Jay.

ARKANSAS All those not protected by federal law are unprotected.

CALIFORNIA Cooper's Hawk, Duck Hawk, Sharp-shinned Hawk, Great Horned Owl, Blue Jay, English Sparrow, House Finch*, Crow, Black-billed Magpie, Shrike*, White Pelican, Cormorant, Blackbird in Districts 1, 2, 3, 4, and 4¾.

COLORADO Eagle (except Bald Eagle), Cooper's Hawk, Duck Hawk, Goshawk, Sharp-shinned Hawk, Great Horned Owl, English Sparrow, Pinion Jay, Magpie, Blue Jay.

CONNECTICUT All hawks, owls, and eagles protected except that hawks may be killed when in the act of destroying poultry. English Sparrow, Crow, Starling, Red-winged Blackbird†, Crow Blackbird†.

DELAWARE Hawks (except Osprey), Turkey Buzzard, Blackbird, Crow, English Sparrow, Starling.

FLORIDA Cooper's Hawk, Goshawk, Sharp-shinned Hawk, Great Horned Owl, English Sparrow, Crow, Jackdaw, Buzzard, Butcher Bird*.

GEORGIA All those not protected by federal laws are unprotected.

IDAHO Those species of hawks and owls that are not "rodent killing" are unprotected. English Sparrow, Crow, Starling, Raven, Kingfisher, Cormorant, Magpie, Pelican.

ILLINOIS Cooper's Hawk, Sharp-shinned Hawk, Great Horned Owl, English Sparrow, European Starling, Crow, Blue Jay, Cowbird, Rusty Blackbird, Bronzed Grackle, Domestic Pigeon.

INDIANA All hawks, owls, and eagles are protected except that "the owner or occupant of the land may kill hawks or owls when in the act of destroying poultry, the property of said owner or occupant, on the land owned or occupied by said owner or occupant." English Sparrow, Starling, Crow.

† When in the act of destroying corn.

IOWA Cooper's Hawk, Sharp-shinned Hawk, Great Horned Owl, European Starling, English Sparrow, Blackbird, Crow.

KANSAS Cooper's Hawk, Goshawk, Sharp-shinned Hawk, Great Horned Owl, Blue Jay, Blackbird, Crow, Starling, English Sparrow.

KENTUCKY Cooper's Hawk, Sharp-shinned Hawk, Great Horned Owl, Crow, Starling, English Sparrow.

LOUISIANA Cooper's Hawk, Duck Hawk, Sharp-shinned Hawk, Great Horned Owl, Cormorant, Vulture, Crow, Red-winged Blackbird, English Sparrow, Starling, Grackle†, Bob-o-link†.

MAINE Hawk, Owl, Kingfisher, Crow, English Sparrow, Cormorant.

MARYLAND Hawk, Owl, Buzzard, Crow, Blue Jay, English Sparrow, Starling, Kingfisher.

MASSACHUSETTS Cooper's Hawk, Goshawk, Sharp-shinned Hawk, Great Horned Owl, English Sparrow, Purple Grackle, Crow, Jay, Starling.

MICHIGAN All hawks, owls, and eagles protected except that "a farmer or landowner may destroy hawks or owls on the land he owns or occupies, which are doing real damage to poultry or other domestic animals." English Sparrow, Blackbird, Starling, Crow.

MINNESOTA Cooper's Hawk, Goshawk, Sharp-shinned Hawk, Great Horned Owl, English Sparrow, Blackbird, Crow, Starling, Magpie, Cormorant.

MISSISSIPPI Cooper's Hawk, Duck Hawk, Sharp-shinned Hawk, Great Horned Owl, English Sparrow, Crow.

MISSOURI Cooper's Hawk, Goshawk, Sharp-shinned Hawk, Great Horned Owl, English Sparrow, European Starling, Crow.

MONTANA Eagle*, Hawk, Great Gray Owl, Great Horned Owl, Snowy Owl, English Sparrow, Crow, Blackbird, Kingfisher, Magpie, Jay.

NEBRASKA Cooper's Hawk, Goshaw, Sharp-shinned Hawk, English Sparrow, Blue Jay, Crow, Magpie, European Starling, Bronzed Grackle.

NEVADA Prairie Falcon, Cooper's Hawk, Duck Hawk, Pigeon Hawk, Western Goshawk, Great Horned Owl, Magpie, Crow, Raven, English Sparrow, Blue Jay, Starling.

NEW HAMPSHIRE Cooper's Hawk, Sharp-shinned Hawk, Barred Owl, Great Horned Owl, Snowy Owl, English Sparrow, European Starling, Crow.

† When destructive to crops.

NEW JERSEY Cooper's Hawk, Goshawk, Sharp-shinned Hawk, Great Horned Owl, English Sparrow, European Starling, Blackbird, Crow.

NEW MEXICO Eagle*, Hawk, Owl, Heron*, Raven, Crow, Magpie.

NEW YORK Cooper's Hawk, Goshawk, Sharp-shinned Hawk, Great Horned Owl, English Sparrow, Starling, Crow, Purple Grackle, Kingfisher.

NORTH CAROLINA Cooper's Hawk, Sharp-shinned Hawk, Great Horned Owl, English Sparrow, Crow, Jay, Blackbird, Starling, Buzzard.

NORTH DAKOTA Sharp-shinned Hawk, Cooper's Hawk, Great Horned Owl, Snowy Owl, Crow, Magpie, Blackbird, English Sparrow, Starling, Cormorant.

OHIO Hawk†, Owl†. European Starling, English Sparrow, Crow, Blackbird.

OKLAHOMA Hawk, Owl, Crow, English Sparrow. Other non-game insectivorous birds not protected by federal law.

OREGON Duck Hawk, Western Goshawk, Cooper's Hawk, Sharp-shinned Hawk, Prairie Falcon, Great Horned Owl, English Sparrow, Cormorant, Crow, Raven, Magpie, Blue Jay, American Merganser, Hooded Merganser, Belted Kingfisher, Ringed Kingfisher, European Starling, Rusty Blackbird.

PENNSYLVANIA Goshawk, Cooper's Hawk, Sharp-shinned Hawk, Great Horned Owl, Snowy Owl, Blue Jay, English Sparrow, European Starling, Kingfisher, Crow.

RHODE ISLAND Hawk (other than Osprey), Owl, English Sparrow, Starling Crow.

SOUTH CAROLINA Eagle (except Bald Eagle), Cooper's Hawk, Duck Hawk, Sharp-shinned Hawk, Great Horned Owl, Buzzard, Crow, English Sparrow Jaybird, Loggerhead*.

SOUTH DAKOTA Cooper's Hawk, Sharp-shinned Hawk, Great Horned Owl, English Sparrow, European Starling, Purple Grackle, Crow, Magpie, Camp Robber, Blue Crow.

TENNESSEE Cooper's Hawk, Sharp-shinned Hawk, Great Horned Owl, English Sparrow, Crow, Crow Blackbird, Starling, Blue Jay, Turkey Buzzard, Black Buzzard, Cormorant.

TEXAS Cooper's Hawk, Duck Hawk, Goshawk, Sharp-shinned Hawk, Great Horned Owl, Golden Eagle, Blackbird, Butcher Bird, Shrike*, Buzzard,

† When doing damage to property.

Vulture, Crow, Jaybird, White Pelican, Raven, Ricebird*, Roadrunner*, Sapsucker*, English Sparrow, Starling, Woodpecker*.

UTAH Cooper's Hawk†, Goshawk†, Prairie Falcon or Bullet Hawk†, Sharp-shinned Hawk†, English Sparrow†, Magpie†, Crow†.

† When causing damage.

VERMONT Cooper's Hawk, Sharp-shinned Hawk, Great Horned Owl, Snowy Owl, English Sparrow, Starling, Crow, Crow Blackbird, Kingfisher.

VIRGINIA Hawk, Owl, Blackbird, Buzzard, Crow, English Sparrow, Jaybird, Starling.

WASHINGTON Cooper's Hawk, Duck Hawk, Pigeon Hawk, Prairie Falcon, Sharp-shinned Hawk, Western Goshawk, Great Horned Owl, Magpie, Crow, English Sparrow, Raven, Starling, Cormorant.

WEST VIRGINIA Cooper's Hawk, Goshawk, Sharp-shinned Hawk, Great Horned Owl, English Sparrow, Starling, Crow, Fish Crow, Cowbird.

WISCONSIN Great Horned Owl, Crow, Starling, Red-winged Blackbird, Cowbird, English Sparrow.

WYOMING Brown Eagle, Golden Eagle, Cooper's Hawk, Duck Hawk, Goshawk, Sharp-shinned Hawk, Great Horned Owl, English Sparrow, Magpie, Kingfisher, Blue Heron*, Crow.

ALASKA Golden Eagle, Hawk, Owl, Crow, Raven, Magpie, Cormorant.

HAWAII All wild birds are protected.

## CANADA

ALBERTA Golden Eagle, English Sparrow, Magpie, Starling.

BRITISH COLUMBIA Goshawk, Cooper's Hawk, Sharp-shinned Hawk, Duck Hawk, Pigeon Hawk, Eagle, Great Horned Owl, Snowy Owl, Raven, Crow, Magpie, Blue Jay, Japanese Starling, English Sparrow.

MANITOBA Goshawk, Sharp-shinned Hawk, Arctic Owl, Crow, Magpie, Cowbird, Blackbird (Grackle), House or English Sparrow.

NEW BRUNSWICK All birds not protected by the Migratory Birds Convention Act except certain game species.

NEWFOUNDLAND Hawk, Great Horned Owl, Crow, Raven, Grackle.

NORTHWEST TERRITORIES All species not protected by Migratory Birds Convention Act or by the local game ordinance.

NOVA SCOTIA Goshawk, Sharp-shinned Hawk, Great Horned Owl, Crow, European Starling, English Sparrow.

ONTARIO Hawk, Owl, Crow, Cowbird, Blackbird, Starling, House Sparrow.

PRINCE EDWARD ISLAND Hawk, Owl, Crow, English Sparrow, Bronzed Grackle, Raven, Starling.

QUEBEC Hawk, Owl, Crow, Starling, English Sparrow, Cormorant, Snow Bunting.

SASKATCHEWAN Snowy Owl, Great Horned Owl, Goshawk, Pigeon Hawk, Duck Hawk, Cooper's Hawk, Sharp-shinned Hawk, Crow, Magpie, Blackbird, Cowbird, Grackle, English Sparrow, Cormorant.

YUKON Golden Eagle, Baldheaded Eagle, All species of Hawk and Falcon (no Raven Hawk found in Yukon), Great Horned Owl, Raven, Magpie.

# Literature Cited

ARNOLD, LEE V., *The Golden Eagle and Its Economic Status*. U. S. Fish and Wildlife Service, Circular 27, Washington, D. C., 1954.

AUDUBON, JOHN J., *The Birds of America*, 1840-1844.
Description of Harris' Hawk.
Description of Harlan's Hawk.
Bald Eagle (Bird of Washington).
Discovery of Caracara.
Voice of Saw-whet Owl.

BAYNARD, OSCAR E., "Predation in the Black Vulture," in *The Oologist*, 1909, pp. 191-193.

BENT, ARTHUR C., *Life Histories of North American Birds of Prey*. U.S. National Museum Bulletin 167, Vol. 1, 1937.
P. 57, on White-tailed Kite eggs.
P. 230, other birds nestings in hawk nests.
P. 228, Swainson Hawk's food.
P. 254, status of Short-tailed Hawk in Florida.

———, *Life Histories of North American Birds of Prey*. U.S. National Museum Bulletin 170, Vol. 2, 1938.
P. 1,    on Gyrfalcons.
P. 27,   quoting F. H. Fowler on Prairie Falcon food.
P. 39,   parasites in Prairie Falcon.
P. 96,   on Aplomado Falcon.
P. 138,  on Guadalupe Caracara.
P. 147,  quoting T. G. Wheelock on food of Barn Owl.
P. 160,  on food of Long-eared Owl.
P. 161,  on "broken wing" act of Long-eared Owl.
P. 162,  quoting W. L. Dawson on Long-eared Owl.
P. 223,  on ability of Richardson's Owl to see in daylight.
P. 225,  quoting W. H. Dall on voice of Richardson's Owl.
P. 228,  on Tengmalm's Owl.
P. 235,  on flight of Saw-Whet Owl.
P. 286,  on Spotted Screech Owl.
P. 295,  quoting E. T. Seton on Great Horned Owl.
P. 306,  on food of Great Horned Owl.

P. 311, on economic status of Great Horned Owl.

P. 316, quoting Otto Widmann on Great Horned Owl.

P. 364, on economic status of Snowy Owl.

P. 376, quoting A. D. Henderson on nesting of Hawk Owl.

P. 377, quoting A. D. Henderson on food of Hawk Owl.

P. 380, quoting E. T. Seton on behavior of Hawk Owl.

P. 401, on size of Pygmy Owl.

P. 439, on Elf Owl habitat.

P. 439, quoting Berry Campbell on Elf Owl habitat.

P. 440, quoting A. J. Van Rossem on Elf Owl.

BROOKS, ALLAN, see MAY JOHN B.

Quoted on food of Marsh Hawk.

CAMERON, E. S., see MAY, JOHN B.

Quoted on food of Marsh Hawk.

CAMPBELL, BERRY, see BENT, ARTHUR C.

Quoted on habitat of Elf Owl.

DALL, W. H., see BENT, ARTHUR C.

Quoted on voice of Richardson's Owl.

DAWSON, W. LEON, *The Birds of California.* South Moulton Co., Los Angeles, 1923.

P. 1673, food of Harris' Hawk.

————, see BENT, ARTHUR C.

Quoted on behavior of Long-eared Owl at nest.

FISHER, A. K., *The Hawks and Owls of North America.* U.S. Department of Agriculture, Bulletin 8, Washington, D.C., 1893.

P. 23,  food of White-tailed Kite.

P. 75,  Swainson's Hawk feeding on ground.

P. 162, flight of Saw-whet Owl.

FORBUSH, EDWARD H., see BENT, ARTHUR C.

Quoted on cannibalistic habit of Barred Owl.

FOWLER, F. H., see BENT, ARTHUR C.

Quoted on food of Prairie Falcon.

HENDERSON, A. D., see BENT, ARTHUR C.

Quoted on American Hawk Owl nesting and food.

JOURDAIN, F. C. R., see MAY, JOHN B.

Quoted on Peale's Falcon.

KOFORD, CARL, *The California Condor.* Research Report No. 4, National Audubon Society, New York, 1953.

MAY, JOHN B., *The Hawks of North America.* National Association of Audubon Societies, New York, 1935.

P. 11,  quoting A. C. Bent on range of White-tailed Kite.

P. 12,   food of Swallow-tailed Kite.
P. 12,   quoting Elliott Coues on Swallow-tailed Kite.
P. 51,   quoted on Zone-tailed Hawk.
P. 59,   quoted on American Rough-legged Hawk.
P. 69,   quoted on Mexican Goshawk.
P. 89,   quoting Robert Ridgway on Marsh Hawk.
P. 89,   quoting H. L. Stoddard on Marsh Hawk.
P. 90,   quoting J. A. Munro on Marsh Hawk.
P. 90,   quoting Allan Brooks on Marsh Hawk.
P. 90,   quoting E. S. Cameron on Marsh Hawk.
P. 90,   quoting Charles Urner on Marsh Hawk.
P. 90,   quoting Norman Criddle on Marsh Hawk.
P. 120, on Prairie Falcon as a bird killer.

MUNRO, J. A., see MAY, JOHN B.
Quoted on food of Marsh Hawk.

REED, CHESTER A., *North American Birds' Eggs*. Doubleday, Page & Co., New York, 1904.
P. 169, description of Duck Hawk eggs.

RIDGWAY, ROBERT, see MAY, JOHN B.
Quoted on food of Marsh Hawk.

SETON, E. T., see BENT, ARTHUR C.
Quoted on nesting and food of Hawk Owl.
Quoted on Great Horned Owl.

SIMMONS, GEORGE F., *Birds of the Austin Region*. University of Texas Press, Austin, 1925.

SPRUNT, JR., ALEXANDER, *The Auk* 57: 564, 1940.
Rough-legged Hawk in Lake Okeechobee, Florida.
———, *Florida Birdlife*. Coward-McCann Co. and National Audubon Society, New York, 1954.
P. 114, Rough-legged Hawk in Florida.
———, and GRIMES, S. A., *An Album of Southern Birds*. University of Texas Press, Austin, 1953.
P. 13, on Great Horned Owl defending nest.

STODDARD, HERBERT L., *The Bob-White Quail*. Charles Scribner's Sons, New York, 1931.
P. 212, Cooper's Hawk in relation to quail.

SWARTH, HARRY S., *Report on a Collection of Birds*. University of California Zoological Publications, Vol. 30, 1926.
P. 64, food of Harlan's Hawk.

TAVERNER, PERCY A., *Birds of Canada* (Revised Edition). Musson Book Co., Ltd., Toronto, 1949.

P. 133, food of Ferruginous Rough-legged Hawk.
THAYER, GERALD H., see MAY, JOHN B.
  Quoted on Duck Hawk.
THOMAS, G. B., see BENT, ARTHUR C.
  Quoted on flight of Mexican Black Hawk.
URNER, CHARLES, see MAY, JOHN B.
  Quoted on food of Marsh Hawk.
VAN ROSSEM, A. J., see BENT, ARTHUR C.
  Quoted on habitat of Elf Owl.
WHEELOCK, T. G., see BENT, ARTHUR C.
  Quoted on food of Barn Owl.
WIDMANN, OTTO, see BENT, ARTHUR C.
  Quoted on Great Horned Owl.